Common Core
Standards Practice Workbook

Grade 4

Teacher Guide

Glenview, Illinois • Boston, Massachusetts
Chandler, Arizona • Upper Saddle River, New Jersey

ALWAYS LEARNING

PEARSON

ISBN-13: 978-0-328-75694-0
ISBN-10:   0-328-75694-6

PEARSON

8 16

Grade 4 Contents

Standards Practice

Assessment

Teacher Support

About this Guide

Pearson is pleased to offer this **Common Core Standards Practice** Teacher's Guide, a companion to the **Common Core Standards Practice Workbook**. It includes these pages:

- **Common Core Standards Practice pages.** Two pages of practice exercises for each Common Core State Standard. Students will find different kinds of exercises that are similar to the items expected to be on the Next Generation Assessment that students will be taking starting in 2014–2015.

- **Practice for the Common Core Assessment.** Each Practice Assessment consists of one (1) Practice End-of-Year Assessment and two (2) Performance Tasks. One Practice Assessment is found in the Student Workbook, while the second is a "secure" test found only in this Teacher's Guide. The two Practice End-of-Year Assessments are mirror assessments.

  The Practice End-of-Year assessment was built to align to the content emphases of both PARCC and SBAC. That means that 70% of the items assess major content emphases. In addition, many of the items are similar to the innovative items that are expected to be on the upcoming Next Generation Assessments. Students will encounter multiple-response selected-response items; simulated technology-enabled items that ask students to sort answer options into appropriate categories or to construct responses on grids, graphs, and number lines; constructed response items that ask them to explain their reasoning or justify their thinking; and extended constructed response items that include multi-part questions with multi-step solutions. The Performance Tasks present students with problem situations in real-world context and ask students to make use of their developing proficiency with the Standards for Mathematical Practice and their firmer understanding of Math Content to find solutions.

- Answers to all of the student pages as 4-ups.

- **Correlation Chart for the Practice EOY Assessment.** The chart indicates for each item the Content Standard assessed and lessons in *enVisionMATH™ Common Core* and sessions in *Investigations in Number, Data, and Space® for the Common Core* where students can go for more practice of the standard assessed.

- **Scoring Rubrics for the four (4) Performance Tasks.** In additional to recommendations for scoring, these pages list both the Standards for Mathematical Practice and Mathematical Content that the task assesses.

Common Core Standards Practice and Assessments

Name _____

Common Core Standards Practice

4.OA.A.1 Interpret a multiplication equation as a comparison, e.g., interpret $35 = 5 \times 7$ as a statement that 35 is 5 times as many as 7 and 7 times as many as 5. Represent verbal statements of multiplicative comparisons as multiplication equations.

1. Which equation shows that 30 is 6 times as many as 5?

    A $11 = 6 + 5$

    B $30 = 6 \times 5$

    C $25 = 5 \times 5$

    D $24 = 30 - 6$

2. Which equation shows that r is 9 times as many as 6?

    A $r = 9 \times 6$

    B $6 \times r = 9$

    C $6 = 9 \times r$

    D $54 = r \times 9 \times 6$

3. Last week, Sharon's mother ordered 60 roses for her shop. This week, she will order 5 times as many roses. How many roses will she order? Write an expression and then find the solution.

4. Aubrey's school has two meeting rooms. The small room seats 25 students. The large room seats three times as many students. How many students does the large room seat? Write an expression and then find the solution.

5. Write a multiplication equation to show that 42 is 7 times as many as 6.

6. Write a multiplication equation to show that 150 is s times as many as 15.

7. Write an equation to find the amount that is 4 times as much as 9.

8. Write an equation to find the amount that is 7 times as much as 8.

9. Write an equation to show that 81 is 9 times *n*.

10. One building has *f* floors. Its taller neighbor has 3 times as many floors. The taller building has 18 floors. Write an equation for *f*, the number of floors in the first building.

11. The students in Mrs. Aubrey's class brought in 15 cans during week 1 of the food drive. During week 2 the students brought in 4 times as many cans. How many cans did the students bring in during week 2?

12. Joey earns $3 each time he walks the Mathers' dog. He earns twice as much when he walks the Randolphs' dog. How much does he earn when he walks the Randolphs' dog? Write an expression that models the comparison.

Name _____

Common Core Standards Practice

4.OA.A.2 Multiply or divide to solve word problems involving multiplicative comparison, e.g., by using drawings and equations with a symbol for the unknown number to represent the problem, distinguishing multiplicative comparison from additive comparison.

1. This year, the music school has 85 students. Last year it had 17 students. How many times greater is this year's number of students?

    a. Write an equation for f.

    b. Solve the equation you wrote.

2. Jennifer bought 12 postcards at a yard sale. Frieda bought 8 times as many postcards.

    a. Write an equation that can be used to find n, the number of postcards that Frieda bought.

    b. Solve the equation you wrote.

3. At the apple orchard, Lisa picks 75 apples. Lisa picks 5 times more apples than Sharon picks.

    a. Write an equation that can be solved for a, the number of apples that Sharon picks.

    b. Solve the equation you wrote.

CC3

4. Janice uses 6 markers for an art project. Ivan uses 4 times as many markers as Janice.

   a. Write an equation to show the number of markers *m* that Ivan uses.

   b. Draw a model to illustrate the equation you wrote.

   c. Solve the equation you wrote.

5. Al sold 19 tickets to the school orchestra concert. Judy sold 3 more tickets than Al. Maria sold 3 times as many tickets as Al.

   a. What operation must you use to find out how many tickets Maria sold? Explain.

   b. Write an expression that you can use to find the number of tickets that Judy sold.

   c. How many tickets did Judy sell?

   d. Write an expression that you can use to find the number of tickets that Maria sold.

   e. How many tickets did Maria sell?

CC 4

Name _____

Common Core Standards Practice

4.OA.A.3 Solve multistep word problems posed with whole numbers and having whole-number answers using the four operations, including problems in which remainders must be interpreted. Represent these problems using equations with a letter standing for the unknown quantity. Assess the reasonableness of answers using mental computation and estimation strategies including rounding.

1. George brought $94 to the shopping mall. He used the money to buy a shirt for $25, a pair of pants for $42, and 2 pairs of socks that each cost $6.

   How much money did George have after he finished shopping at the mall?

2. Nancy chopped the vegetables shown in the table, then mixed them into a salad. She divided the salad equally into 5 containers.

Broccoli	2 cups
Cauliflower	1 cup
Green peppers	2 cups
Red peppers	1 cup
Cucumbers	3 cups
Lettuce	6 cups

   How many cups of vegetables did Nancy put in each container?

3. At the school carnival, students sold 483 hamburgers for $4 each and 214 hot dog for $2 each.

   a. Write an equation to find how much money they took in from the sale of hamburgers. Use the letter *h* to represent the unknown amount. Then solve the equation.

   b. Write an equation to find how much money they took in from the sale of hot dogs. Use the letter *d* to represent the unknown amount. Then solve the equation.

   c. How much money did they take in from the hamburgers and hot dogs?

4. The Walters family bought 3 ham sandwiches and 4 fruit cups for lunch. Each sandwich cost $4 and each fruit cup cost $2. How much did the family spend on lunch?

5. Volunteers at the park will plant 150 marigold plants and 60 petunia plants. They will plant 5 rows of petunias and twice as many rows of marigolds.

   a. How many rows of marigolds will the volunteers plant?

   b. How many petunias will they plant in each row?

6. Mr. Chen wants to buy 27 blue pens and 35 red pens. The pens are sold in packages of 8.

   a. How many packages of blue pens must he buy? Write an equation using the letter *b* for the unknown amount. Then solve the equation.

   b. How many packages of red pens will Mr. Chen buy? Write an equation and use the letter *r* for the unknown amount. Then solve the equation.

   c. One package of pens costs $2. How much will Mr. Chen spend on pens?

Name _____

Common Core Standards Practice

4.OA.B.4 Find all factor pairs for a whole number in the range 1–100. Recognize that a whole number is a multiple of each of its factors. Determine whether a given whole number in the range 1–100 is a multiple of a given one-digit number. Determine whether a given whole number in the range 1–100 is prime or composite.

1. Which of these are prime numbers? Circle all of the numbers that are prime.

17	37	38
45	57	59
63	84	89

2. Which of these numbers are composite? Circle all of the numbers that are composite.

2	5	9
19	33	45
53	69	91

3. Which of these numbers is a multiple of 8? Circle all of the numbers that are multiples of 8.

2	3	4
16	20	32
36	48	54
56	68	

4. Which set of numbers are all factors of 50?

   A 1, 2, 5, 10, 25, 50
   B 1, 2, 8, 12, 24, 50
   C 1, 4, 5, 10, 12, 50
   D 1, 4, 5, 9, 10, 50

5. Is 39 a prime or composite number? Explain how you know.

6. List four multiples of 9.

CC 7

7. Write all of the factor pairs for 28.

8. The number 36 is a multiple of several numbers. List all of them.

9. Which of these numbers are prime? Which are composite? Put an X on the prime numbers. Circle the composite numbers. In the space below, write the factors of each number that you identified as composite.

3	13	23	33	43
53	63	73	83	93

10. What is the only even prime number? Explain how you know.

11. Answer each question. Explain how you know.

Is 81 a multiple of 3?

Is 46 a multiple of 4?

Is 55 a multiple of 7?

Is 72 a multiple of 9?

Is 45 a multiple of 6?

Name _____

Common Core Standards Practice

4.OA.C.5 Generate a number or shape pattern that follows a given rule. Identify apparent features of the pattern that were not explicit in the rule itself.

1. Continue the pattern below. Use the rule, "Add 4."

   4, _____, _____, _____, _____, _____

   What do you notice about the digits in the ones place?

2. Draw shapes to continue the pattern. Use the rule, "Add one side to the shape."

   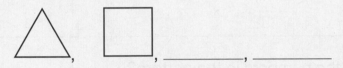
   , _____, _____

3. Continue the pattern below. Use the rule, "Divide by 2."

   96, _____, _____, _____, _____, _____

4. a. Continue the pattern below. Use the rule, "Move the dot around the square."

   b. Look closely. What pattern do you see that is not mentioned in the rule?

5. a. Complete the number sequence below by using the rule, "Subtract 5."

50, _____, _____, _____, _____, _____, _____

b. What do you notice about the digits in the ones place?

6. a. Complete the number sequence below by using the rule, "Add 2."

3, _____, _____, _____, _____, _____, _____

b. What do you notice about the numbers in the pattern?

7. Complete the pattern by using the rule, "Add a dot to the square."

 , _____, _____, _____

Name _____

Common Core Standards Practice

4.NBT.A.1 Recognize that in a multi-digit whole number, a digit in one place represents ten times what it represents in the place to its right.

1. Jonah wrote a 5-digit number on a piece of paper. He gave his friend Marbey these clues to find the number.

   a. The 4 is in the place that is ten times greater than the place where the 2 is.

   b. The 2 is in the place that is one hundred times less than the place where the 5 is.

   c. The 6 is in the place that is ten times less than the place where the 2 is.

   d. The 1 is in the place that is ten times greater than the place where the 5 is.

   What is the number?

2. Which of these statements is true about the number shown.

   169,961

   A The first 9 represents a value ten times greater than the second 9.

   B The first 9 represents a value one hundred times greater than the second 9.

   C The first 6 represents a value ten times greater than the second 6.

   D The first 6 represents a value one hundred times greater than the second 6.

3. Look at the number below.

   75,575

   a. How many times does the digit 5 appear in the number?

   b. How do the values of the digit 5 differ in the number?

   c. How much greater is the value of the first 5 compared to the value of the second 5?

   d. How much greater is the value of the second 5 compared to the value of the third 5?

4. Which of these statements is true about the number shown?

78,409

A The 7 represents a value that is 10 times greater than the 4.

B The 4 represents a value that is 10 times greater than the 9.

C The 8 represents a value that is 10 times greater than the 4.

D The 8 represents a value that is 2 times greater than the 4.

5. Minah gives the following clues about a 5-digit number.

a. The 8 is in a place that is 100 times greater than the place of the 2.

b. The 2 is in a place that is 100 times greater than the place of the 0.

c. The 3 is in a place that is 10 times less than the place of the 8.

d. The 5 is in a place that is 100 times less than the place of the 3.

What is the number?

6. Look at the number below.

38,108

a. How many times does the digit 8 appear in the number?

b. How do the values of the digit 8 differ in the number?

c. How much greater is the value of the first 8 compared to the value of the second 8?

d. Write a number with the same digits, but make the place of the first 8 be 10 times the place of the second 8.

Name _____

Common Core Standards Practice

4.NBT.A.2 Read and write multi-digit whole numbers using base-ten numerals, number names, and expanded form. Compare two multi-digit numbers based on meanings of the digits in each place, using >, =, and < symbols to record the results of comparisons.

1. What is 3,106 in expanded form?

   A 3,000 + 100 + 6

   B 3,000 + 10 + 6

   C 3,000 + 6

   D 3,000 + 100 + 60

2. Thirty-five thousand, four hundred seventeen people attended a county fair. What is this number in standard form?

   A 35,174

   B 35,417

   C 35,470

   D 35,471

3. What is 9,000 + 800 + 30 + 1 in standard form?

   A 9,031

   B 9,138

   C 9,381

   D 9,831

4. Which symbol should replace the circle to make the number sentence true?

   438 ◯ 400 + 30 + 8

   A <

   B ≠

   C =

   D >

5. Write 4,230 in expanded form.

6. Write a number sentence to compare 89,723 and 89,372. Use the < symbol.

Explain how you know which number is greater.

CC13

7. A group of 246 people attend the school play. Write this number in words.

8. Write twenty-seven thousand, six hundred twelve in expanded form.

9. Dali sold one hundred fourteen tickets for the fundraiser. Sharon sold 141. Who sold more tickets? Write a number sentence to show your answer.

10. Write 3,406 in words and in expanded form.

11. Write a number sentence that compares 58,219 and 58,231.

Explain how you knew which symbol to use.

12. What symbol should replace the circle to make the number sentence true?

1,998 ◯ two thousand fourteen

Explain how you knew which symbol to use.

Name _____

Common Core Standards Practice

4.NBT.A.3 Use place value understanding to round multi-digit whole numbers to any place.

1. What is 192 rounded to the nearest ten?

    A 100

    B 180

    C 190

    D 200

2. Which number rounds to 5,600 when it is rounded to the nearest hundred?

    A 5,674

    B 5,637

    C 5,549

    D 5,512

3. The school talent show raised $2,914. What is this amount rounded to the nearest thousand and to the nearest hundred?

4. What is 6,708 rounded to the nearest ten?

5. On Thursday, 45 students walked to school. What is this number rounded to the nearest ten?

6. Aisha thinks that 1,275 rounded to the nearest hundred is 1,200 because "2 is less than 5."

    a. What might be Aisha's misunderstanding about rounding?

    b. Help Aisha correct her misunderstanding by explaining rounding.

7. The population of Centerville is 89,582. What is the population rounded to the nearest thousand?

  A 90,000

  B 89,600

  C 89,500

  D 89,000

8. A newspaper reported that about 27,000 people attended a major league baseball game. If the actual attendance was rounded to the nearest thousand, how many people could have attended the game?

  A 27,942

  B 27,610

  C 26,789

  D 26,495

9. Write a number that would round to 5,000 when it is rounded to the nearest thousand.

10. Write two numbers that round to 150 when they are rounded to the nearest ten.

11. The attendance at an amusement park during the month of July was 174,383. What is the attendance rounded to the nearest thousand?

12. Ken says that 9,138 rounded to the nearest thousand is 9,100 because "3 is less than 5."

  a. What might be Ken's misunderstanding about rounding?

  b. Help Ken correct his misunderstanding.

Name _____

Common Core Standards Practice

4.NBT.B.4 Fluently add and subtract multi-digit whole numbers using the standard algorithm.

1. Use the information in the table to answer each question below.

City	Population (2010)
Gulfport, MS	67,793
Redlands, CO	8,685
Rocky River, OH	20,213

a. In 2000, the population of Gulfport, MS, was 71,127. How many more people lived in Gulfport, MS, in 2000 than in 2010?

b. In 2010, how many more people lived in Rocky River, OH, than in Redlands, CO?

c. In 2010, what was the total population of the three cities listed in the table?

2. Find the sum.

    4,068
 + 2,291

3. Find the difference.

  500,000
 − 184,875

4. Students at the Lincoln Elementary School are selling tickets to the school spring fair. The third graders have sold 1,673 tickets. The fourth graders have sold 3,098 tickets. What is the total number of tickets the students in both classes have sold?

A 1,425

B 4,671

C 4,771

D 5,771

5. A cowgirl spends $995 on a used trail saddle. She also spends $360 on new saddlebags. How much does she spend in all?

A $1,365

B $1,355

C $1,255

D $635

6. Miles is 1,196 weeks old. His younger sister Abby is 468 weeks old.

a. Write and solve an equation to show the difference in their ages in weeks.

b. Write and solve an equation to show their total ages.

Name _____

Common Core Standards Practice

4.NBT.B.5 Multiply a whole number of up to four digits by a one-digit whole number, and multiply two two-digit numbers, using strategies based on place value and the properties of operations. Illustrate and explain the calculation by using equations, rectangular arrays, and/or area models.

1. Find the product.

$$\begin{array}{r} 2{,}056 \\ \times \quad 9 \\ \hline \end{array}$$

2. Find the product.

$$\begin{array}{r} 89 \\ \times \ 27 \\ \hline \end{array}$$

3. Hannah is helping her grandmother make a quilt. Each row will have 16 squares. There will be 14 rows.

    a. Draw a model of the quilt.

    b. How many squares will Hannah and her grandmother need to make?

4. Juan bakes and sells dog treats at the farmers market. He always fits 12 treats on a cookie sheet. On Saturday, he bakes 8 batches of dog treats.

   a. Draw an array to match the problem situation.

   b. Write an equation to show how many dog treats Juan bakes.

   c. Solve the equation you wrote.

5. An Olympic-sized swimming pool is 50 meters long and 25 meters wide.

   a. Draw a model to show the area of an Olympic-sized pool.

   b. Write an equation to show the area of an Olympic-sized pool.

   c. Solve the equation you wrote.

6. Principal Watts walks 5 miles every day. How many miles does he walk in 1 year, or 365 days? Write and solve an equation.

Name _____

Common Core Standards Practice

4.NBT.B.6 Find whole-number quotients and remainders with up to four-digit dividends and one-digit divisors, using strategies based on place value, the properties of operations, and/or the relationship between multiplication and division. Illustrate and explain the calculation by using equations, rectangular arrays, and/or area models.

1. Find the quotient.

$486 \div 3$

2. Find the quotient.

$1{,}250 \div 7$

3. Aaron raises chickens. He sells chicken eggs by the dozen. On Friday, Aaron sold 96 eggs. How many dozen eggs did Aaron sell?

a. Draw a rectangular array to model the problem situation.

b. Write an equation that matches the model you drew.

c. Solve the equation you wrote.

4. Claire helps at her mother's flower shop. This week, her mother received a shipment of 250 sunflowers. Claire put them in bundles of 8 flowers. How many bundles did she make? Did she have any bundles with fewer than 8 sunflowers? If so, how many more sunflowers would she need to complete the bundle?

5. A tailor sews 8 buttons on each jacket he makes. He has 220 buttons. On how many jackets can he sew buttons?

6. Green Valley City Park has an area of 6,557 square feet. The length of the park is 83 feet.

   a. Draw a model to show Green Valley City Park.

   b. Write and solve an equation to show how to find the width of the park.

Name _____

Common Core Standards Practice

4.NF.A.1 Explain why a fraction $\frac{a}{b}$ is equivalent to a fraction $\frac{(n \times a)}{(n \times b)}$ by using visual fraction models, with attention to how the number and size of the parts differ even though the two fractions themselves are the same size. Use this principle to recognize and generate equivalent fractions.

1. Stella and Brian each heat up a small pizza. Stella cuts her pizza into 4 equal slices. Brian cuts his pizza into 8 equal parts.

   a. Draw models of Stella's pizza and Brian's pizza.

   b. Stella eats two pieces of her pizza. Brian eats four pieces of his pizza. Do they eat the same amount of pizza? Show using models.

2. Which of the fractions below is equivalent to $\frac{1}{3}$? Show why that fraction is equivalent to $\frac{1}{3}$.

   $\frac{4}{5}$ $\frac{4}{6}$ $\frac{4}{9}$ $\frac{4}{12}$

3. Which two models show equivalent fractions? Explain how you know.

A   B   C

4. Four students draw a design for a class flag. Each flag is black and white. Shown below are four designs. Which designs have the same fractions of black and white? Explain how you know.

Madison's design

Kyle's design

Jason's design

Lina's design

Name _____

Common Core Standards Practice

4.NF.A.2 Compare two fractions with different numerators and different denominators, e.g., by creating common denominators or numerators, or by comparing to a benchmark fraction such as $\frac{1}{2}$. Recognize that comparisons are valid only when the two fractions refer to the same whole. Record the results of comparisons with symbols >, =, or <, and justify the conclusions, e.g., by using a visual fraction model.

1. Which fraction is less than $\frac{5}{8}$?

   A $\frac{7}{8}$

   B $\frac{6}{8}$

   C $\frac{5}{6}$

   D $\frac{4}{8}$

2. Which fraction is greater than $\frac{1}{7}$?

   A $\frac{1}{5}$

   B $\frac{1}{8}$

   C $\frac{1}{9}$

   D $\frac{1}{10}$

3. A kitchen floor has green, yellow, and white tiles. Of those tiles, $\frac{2}{5}$ are green and $\frac{2}{10}$ are yellow. Are there more green tiles than yellow tiles? Explain how you know.

4. Barry got a small sandwich for lunch and ate $\frac{1}{2}$ of his sandwich. Jonah got a large sandwich and ate $\frac{1}{2}$ of his sandwich. Did Jonah and Barry eat the same amount for lunch? Explain how you know.

5. Place these fractions on the number line below. Then complete the inequalities.

$\frac{2}{5}$ $\frac{1}{4}$ $\frac{4}{6}$ $\frac{5}{8}$

0        $\frac{1}{2}$ $\frac{2}{2}$

a. $\frac{2}{5}$ _____ $\frac{1}{2}$ and $\frac{4}{6}$ _____ $\frac{1}{2}$ so $\frac{2}{5}$ _____ $\frac{4}{6}$.

b. $\frac{5}{8}$ _____ $\frac{1}{2}$ and $\frac{1}{4}$ _____ $\frac{1}{2}$ so $\frac{5}{8}$ _____ $\frac{1}{4}$.

c. $\frac{4}{6}$ _____ $\frac{1}{2}$ and $\frac{4}{6}$ _____ $\frac{2}{2}$ and $\frac{5}{8}$ _____ $\frac{1}{2}$ and $\frac{5}{8}$ _____ $\frac{2}{2}$ and $\frac{5}{8}$ _____ $\frac{4}{6}$.

6. Tell which fraction is greater: $\frac{6}{8}$ _____ $\frac{6}{10}$. Write < or >.

Draw models of fraction strips to prove your answer.

7. Inez compared the fractions $\frac{1}{5}$ and $\frac{1}{3}$. She said, "I compared the denominators. Because 5 is greater than 3, $\frac{1}{5}$ is greater than $\frac{1}{3}$."

Is Inez correct? Explain your answer.

Name _____

Common Core Standards Practice

4.NF.B.3a Understand addition and subtraction of fractions as joining and separating parts referring to the same whole.

1. Nan drew a model to show the addition of two fractions.

   Write an equation to match Nate's model.

   _____ + _____ = _____

2. Amy runs $\frac{2}{5}$ of a mile. Then she walks another $\frac{2}{5}$ of a mile.

   a. How far does Amy run and walk? Use the number line to model the problem.

   b. Write and solve an equation to match your model.

   _____ + _____ = _____

3. Mr. Kopek cuts a pie into 8 equal pieces. He eats two pieces and his son eats three pieces.

   a. What fraction of the pie do Mr. Kopek and his son eat? Draw a model to match the problem.

   b. Write an equation to match your model.

   _____ + _____ = _____

CC 27

4. Kyle draws a model to show the subtraction of two fractions.

Write an equation to match the model.

_____ − _____ = _____

5. Fen bought $\frac{3}{4}$ yard of cloth. She used $\frac{1}{4}$ yard to make a napkin. How much cloth does she have left?

6. In spring, Toni divided her vegetable garden into 3 equal sections. She planted beans in one section, corn in the second section, and squash in the third section. One day in autumn, Toni harvested all the beans and squash.

a. Draw a model to match the problem situation.

b. What fraction of the garden has Toni not yet harvested?

_____ − _____ = _____

Name _____

Common Core Standards Practice

4.NF.B.3b Decompose a fraction into a sum of fractions with the same denominator in more than one way, recording each decomposition by an equation. Justify decompositions, e.g., by using a visual fraction model.

1. Jiro thinks of a fraction. He decomposes the fraction into three fractions shown below.

   $\frac{1}{6} + \frac{1}{6} + \frac{3}{6}$

   What fraction is Jiro thinking of? Tell how you know.

2. Chloe uses fractions strips to show $\frac{7}{8}$ as the sum of fractions.

1							
$\frac{1}{8}$	$\frac{1}{8}$	$\frac{1}{8}$	$\frac{1}{8}$	$\frac{1}{8}$	$\frac{1}{8}$	$\frac{1}{8}$	$\frac{1}{8}$

   Draw another way to show $\frac{7}{8}$ as the sum of fractions.

   Write an equation to match your models.

3. Write $\frac{7}{8}$ as the sum of unit fractions.

4. Write $1\frac{2}{3}$ as the sum of two fractions that have the same denominator.

Write $1\frac{2}{3}$ as the sum of a whole number and two fractions that have the same denominator.

5. To show a fraction, George placed these fraction strips on his desk.

What fraction does his model show? Write the fraction as a sum of the fractions in the model.

Name _____

Common Core Standards Practice

4.NF.B.3c Add and subtract mixed numbers with like denominators, e.g., by replacing each mixed number with an equivalent fraction, and/or by using properties of operations and the relationship between addition and subtraction.

Find the sum or difference. Explain how you found the sum or difference.

1. $3\frac{1}{4} + 2\frac{3}{4} =$

2. $4\frac{5}{6} - 3\frac{1}{6} =$

3. Sherri swam $2\frac{5}{8}$ miles on Monday. She swam $1\frac{1}{8}$ miles on Wednesday.

   a. How many miles did Sherri swim on Monday and Wednesday?

   b. How many more miles did Sherri swim on Monday than on Wednesday? Write an equation and solve.

4. What is the sum of $10\frac{3}{5}$ and $6\frac{3}{5}$?

   A 4

   B $\frac{166}{5}$

   C $16\frac{1}{5}$

   D $17\frac{1}{5}$

CC 31

5. What addition sentence does the model show?

_____ + _____ = _____

6. Subtract. Explain how you found the difference.

$$9\frac{1}{3}$$
$$-\ 1\frac{2}{3}$$

7. Check your answer to problem 6 by adding. Explain how you found your work.

Name _____

Common Core Standards Practice

4.NF.B.3d Solve word problems involving addition and subtraction of fractions referring to the same whole and having like denominators, e.g., by using visual fraction models and equations to represent the problem.

1. Georgia is mixing colors to paint a door. She pours $\frac{3}{8}$ cup of red paint into a can. Then she adds $\frac{2}{8}$ cup of blue paint to the can.

   a. How much paint is in the can? Write an equation.

   b. Solve your equation.

2. A piece of tape is $\frac{10}{12}$ inch long. Diego cuts off $\frac{5}{12}$ inch of the piece of tape.

   a. Use the number line to show a model of the problem.

   b. How much tape is left?

3. Erika lives on a farm. Her father uses $\frac{1}{8}$ of the farm land to grow soy beans and $\frac{3}{8}$ of the farm land to grow corn. The rest of the farm land is used as grazing land for cattle.

a. Draw a model to match the problem.

b. What fraction of the farm land is used to grow crops (corn and soy beans)?

c. What fraction of the farm land is used for cattle grazing?

4. Jamal spends $\frac{3}{4}$ of an hour writing a short story. Then he spends $\frac{1}{4}$ of an hour revising the story. How much longer does Jamal spend writing than revising? Write and solve an equation.

Name _____

Common Core Standards Practice

4.NF.B.4a Understand a fraction $\frac{a}{b}$ as a multiple of $\frac{1}{b}$.

1.

$\frac{1}{4}$	$\frac{1}{4}$	$\frac{1}{4}$	$\frac{1}{4}$

   a. How many sections are shaded? _____

   b. What fraction of the model is shaded? _____

2.

$\frac{1}{5}$	$\frac{1}{5}$	$\frac{1}{5}$	$\frac{1}{5}$	$\frac{1}{5}$

   a. How many sections are shaded? _____

   b. What fraction of the model is shaded? _____

3. Shade parts of the circle to model the fraction $\frac{5}{6}$.

   How many parts did you shade? _____

4. Draw a model to show three equal parts of a whole.
Then shade parts of the model to show $\frac{2}{3}$.

   How many parts did you shade? _____

CC 35

5. Julie divides a board into 8 equal pieces. Draw a model to show Julie's board.

    a. Julie paints $\frac{4}{8}$ of the board.
       How many pieces of the board does she paint? _____

    b. How many pieces of the board are not painted? _____

       What fraction of the board do the unpainted pieces represent? _____

6. Jorge divides a circle into 12 equal slices. Draw a model to match.

    a. Jorge cuts out $\frac{3}{12}$ of the circle.
       How many slices of the circle does he cut out? _____

    b. How many slices of the circle are left? _____

       What fraction of the circle remains? _____

Name _____

Common Core Standards Practice

4.NF.B.4b Understand a multiple of $\frac{a}{b}$ as a multiple of $\frac{1}{b}$, and use this understanding to multiply a fraction by a whole number.

1. What is $4 \times \frac{3}{4}$? Explain how you know.

2. What is $2 \times \frac{3}{8}$? Explain how you know.

3. What is $5 \times \frac{2}{3}$? Explain how you know.

4. What is $4 \times \frac{2}{3}$?

5. Find $\frac{5}{6} \times 7$.

6. Multiply $\frac{3}{7}$ and 5.

7. Multiply $\frac{4}{7}$ and 2.

8. What is $3 \times \frac{4}{3}$?

9. What is $5 \times \frac{8}{9}$?

10. Multiply $\frac{3}{5}$ and 6.

11. Multiply $\frac{2}{9}$ and 7.

Name _____

Common Core Standards Practice

4.NF.B.4c Solve word problems involving multiplication of a fraction by a whole number, e.g., by using visual fraction models and equations to represent the problem.

1. Fern is helping her mother make decorations for a family gathering. Fern is putting lace around napkins. For each napkin, Fern needs $\frac{3}{5}$ yard of lace. Fern will put the lace on 10 napkins.

    a. Use a number line model to show the problem.

    b. Write an equation to match the model. Use the letter *l* to represent the amount of lace that Fern will need.

    c. How many yards of lace will Fern need? Explain your answer.

2. Mindy wants to paint her room. Her mother tells her that she will need $\frac{2}{3}$ gallon of paint for each of the 4 walls. How much paint will she need?

    a. Draw a model to match the problem.

    b. Write an equation to match the model. Use the letter *p* to represent the amount of paint Mindy will need.

    c. How many gallons of paint will Mindy need to buy? Explain your answer.

3. Vicki has a vegetable garden. She spends $\frac{3}{4}$ hour in her vegetable garden each weekend. How many hours will she spend in her garden over the 12 weeks of summer?

    a. Use a number line model to show the problem.

    b. Write an equation to match the model. Use the letter h to represent the number of hours that Vicki will spend in her garden.

    c. How many hours will Vicki spend in the garden? Explain your answer.

4. Frank plays in a soccer league. At each practice, he drinks $\frac{3}{5}$ gallon of sports drink. He practices 5 days a week. How many gallons of sports drink does his mother need to buy each week?

Name _____

Common Core Standards Practice

4.NF.C.5 Express a fraction with denominator 10 as an equivalent fraction with denominator 100, and use this technique to add two fractions with respective denominators 10 and 100.

1. For each of these fractions, write the equivalent fraction with a denominator of 100.

$\frac{4}{10}$ = _____ $\frac{7}{10}$ = _____

$\frac{2}{10}$ = _____ $\frac{9}{10}$ = _____

$\frac{18}{10}$ = _____ $\frac{26}{10}$ = _____

2. Find the sums.

a. $\frac{4}{10} + \frac{3}{100}$ = _____

b. $\frac{7}{10} + \frac{2}{100}$ = _____

c. $\frac{9}{10} + \frac{3}{100}$ = _____

d. $\frac{1}{100} + \frac{5}{10}$ = _____

e. $\frac{6}{100} + \frac{8}{10}$ = _____

Find the sums.

3. $\dfrac{5}{10} + \dfrac{2}{100} =$ _____

4. $\dfrac{7}{100} + \dfrac{2}{10} =$ _____

5. $\dfrac{8}{10} + \dfrac{3}{100} =$ _____

6. $\dfrac{4}{100} + \dfrac{3}{10} =$ _____

7. $\dfrac{6}{100} + \dfrac{1}{10} =$ _____

8. $\dfrac{36}{10} + \dfrac{8}{100} =$ _____

9. $\dfrac{11}{10} + \dfrac{7}{100} =$ _____

10. $\dfrac{5}{100} + \dfrac{2}{10} =$ _____

Name _____

Common Core Standards Practice

4.NF.C.6 Use decimal notation for fractions with denominators 10 or 100.

1. Which is the decimal form of $\frac{4}{10}$?

    A 0.4

    B 4.0

    C 0.04

    D 0.44

2. Which fraction equals 0.29?

    A $\frac{2}{9}$

    B $\frac{2}{10}$

    C $\frac{29}{100}$

    D $\frac{29}{10}$

3. Write these fractions in decimal form.

$\frac{2}{10}$ = _____

$\frac{5}{10}$ = _____

$\frac{22}{100}$ = _____

$\frac{78}{100}$ = _____

$\frac{45}{100}$ = _____

$\frac{92}{100}$ = _____

4. Write these decimals as fractions. Use denominators of either 10 or 100.

0.3 = _____

0.18 = _____

0.73 = _____

0.8 = _____

0.48 = _____

0.67 = _____

CC 43

5. The number line shows tenths from 0 to 1.

0   0.3   1

a. Write decimals to complete the number line.

b. Below the number line, add leaders and labels for these three numbers: 0.68, 0.25, and 0.82.

6. The number line shows tenths from 0 to 1.

A   D   C   B

0   0.5   1

What decimals are shown by the short lines with letters? If you are not sure, write your best estimate.

Line A: _____

Line B: _____

Line C: _____

Line D: _____

Why is it difficult to identify lines C and D exactly?

CC 44

Name _____

Common Core Standards Practice

4.NF.C.7 Compare two decimals to hundredths by reasoning about their size. Recognize that comparisons are valid only when the two decimals refer to the same whole. Record the results of comparisons with the symbols >, =, or <, and justify the conclusions, e.g., by using a visual model.

1. Plot these two decimals on the number line below.

   0.43   0.39

   Write an inequality comparing the two decimals. Explain your answer using the number line.

2. Plot these two decimals on the number line below.

   0.28   0.82

   Write an inequality comparing the two decimals. Explain your answer using the number line.

3. The baseball team started the game with two one-liter bottles of water. At the end of the game, the first bottle had 0.3 liters left and the second had 0.4 liters left.

Draw a model to show the amount of water left in each bottle after the game.

Out of which liter bottle did more player take water? the first or the second?

4. Simon and Danielle are on the baseball team. Last season, 0.15 of Simon's hits were home runs, and 0.15 of Danielle's hits were also home runs.

a. Can you tell whether Simon and Danielle hit the same number of home runs?

b. Frank is also on the baseball team. Of his hits last season, 0.19 were home runs. Can you tell if he hit more home runs than Simon or Danielle? Explain.

5. Draw a decimal square to represent 0.33 and 0.27.

Which is greater?

_____ < _____

Name _____

Common Core Standards Practice

4.MD.A.1 Know relative sizes of measurement units within one system of units including km, m, cm; kg, g; lb, oz.; l, ml; hr, min, sec. Within a single system of measurement, express measurements in a larger unit in terms of a smaller unit. Record measurement equivalents in a two-column table.

1. A distance of 5 kilometers (km) is the same as how many meters (m)?

   A 50 m

   B 500 m

   C 5,000 m

   D 50,000 m

2. A movie lasts 3 hours. How many minutes is this?

   A 30 minutes

   B 60 minutes

   C 120 minutes

   D 180 minutes

3. Change each of these measurements into a smaller unit.

   7 kilograms into grams _____

   5 pounds into ounces _____

   12 meters into centimeters _____

   6 hours into minutes _____

   9 minutes into seconds _____

   2 pound into ounces _____

   4 yards into feet _____

4. Decide whether each equation is true or false. If the statement is false, then write the corrected equation on the line to the right.

4 kilometers = 4,000 meters _____

10 pounds = 80 ounces _____

2 minutes = 90 seconds _____

15 liters = 0.15 milliliters _____

3 hours = 180 minutes _____

10 minutes = 300 seconds _____

17 kilograms = 1,700 grams _____

7 meters = 700 centimeters _____

5. Frieda worked on her homework last night for 120 minutes. How many hours did she spend on her homework last night?

6. A scientist measures 5 liters of water in a beaker. How many milliliters of water did the scientist measure in the beaker?

7. How many seconds are in 1 hour? Explain how you know.

Name _____

Common Core Standards Practice

4.MD.A.2 Use the four operations to solve word problems involving distances, intervals of time, liquid volumes, masses of objects, and money, including problems involving simple fractions or decimals, and problems that require expressing measurements given in a larger unit in terms of a smaller unit. Represent measurement quantities using diagrams such as number line diagrams that feature a measurement scale.

1. Martha and her family went to the seashore for a week-long vacation. For 5 days of their vacation, they rode bicycles around the area. The table below shows how far they rode each day.

Day	Miles
Monday	5
Tuesday	7
Wednesday	5
Thursday	8
Friday	5

a. How many miles did they ride during their week-long vacation?

b. What was the difference between the longest and the shortest ride?

c. Martha wanted to ride an average of 7 miles a day during the family vacation. To find the average, she took the total number of miles they rode and divided it by the 5 days. What did she find? Did she make her goal?

2. A scientist is carrying out an experiment. She measures 30 milliliters of liquid and pours it into a 100-milliliter beaker. Later, she adds another 25 milliliters of liquid to the beaker. How much more liquid can the scientist add to the beaker?

3. Micah and his father did some laundry at the laundromat. To wash a load costs $2 and to dry a load costs another $2. Micah and his father washed and dried 4 loads of laundry. They also had to buy 4 packets of detergent for $1 per packet.

How much did Micah and his father spend to do their laundry?

4. During the rainy season, the height of a river increases 70 centimeters a day. After how many days will the river increase a total of 3.5 meters?

CC 49

5. Jeremiah is making a care package for his sister who is away at college. He can send up to 5 pounds for a flat rate of $12.95. He puts some items in the box and then weighs it. It weighs $2\frac{3}{8}$ pounds. He has more items he would like to send. What else can he add to the box to be as close to 5 pounds without going over? What is the weight of the box with the additional items?

Item	Weight
2 small boxes of dark chocolate truffles	$1\frac{2}{8}$ pound per box
3 packets of candied fruit	$\frac{6}{8}$ pound per packet
2 packet of hair clips	$\frac{1}{8}$ pound per packet
1 small bottle of body lotion	$\frac{5}{8}$ pound per bottle

6. a. Sam has a piggy bank full of quarters, dimes, nickels, and pennies. Describe two ways he could make $0.78 using only two kinds of coins.

b. Which coin must be used in both ways?

7. Naomi stops every 600 meters as she walks a distance of 2.4 kilometers. How many stops does she make?

8. At Hogan Airport, an airplane takes off every 12 minutes. How many airplanes take off in 5 hours?

Name _____

Common Core Standards Practice

4.MD.A.3 Apply the area and perimeter formulas for rectangles in real world and mathematical problems.

1. Teresa measures the dimensions of her math book. It is 28 centimeters long and 21 centimeters wide. How can Teresa find the perimeter of her math book?

2. Ted is helping his father plant their vegetable garden this year. They will put a fence around the garden. Ted measures the length of the garden, which is 6 feet. His father tells him that the width is twice the length. How much fencing do Ted and his father need to buy to enclose the garden?

A 36 feet

B 24 feet

C 12 feet

D 6 feet

3. The area of a rectangular bedroom is 240 square feet. If the length of the bedroom is 16 feet, what is the width?

4. The model below shows the floor plan of a room. What is the area of the room? Explain how you found your answer.

5. A rectangular piece of construction paper is 11 inches long and 8 inches wide. How could it be cut to make a rectangle that has an area of 32 square inches?

6. Tasha is decorating a rectangular bulletin board by putting ribbon around its outer edge. The bulletin board is 14 inches wide and 18 inches tall. How many inches of ribbon does she need?

7. Janice walked around two sides of a square park. The perimeter of the park is 1,200 yards. How many yards did Janice walk? Explain your answer.

8. Joey's playhouse has a perimeter of 28 feet. What could be the dimensions of the playhouse? Draw a model and label the length and width. Show that the dimensions equal a perimeter of 28 feet.

9. Roger just got a new puppy for his birthday. He and his mother will build a fence around an area in the backyard for the puppy to play in. The play area will be 24 square feet. What dimensions could the play area be? Which dimensions would require the least amount of fencing?

Name _____

Common Core Standards Practice

4.MD.B.4 Make a line plot to display a data set of measurements in fractions of a unit ($\frac{1}{2}$, $\frac{1}{4}$, $\frac{1}{8}$). Solve problems involving addition and subtraction of fractions by using information presented in line plots.

1. Ryan's dog just had a litter of 8 puppies. His mother measured the length each of the puppies. The table below shows their lengths in inches.

Puppy	1	2	3	4	5	6	7	8
Length in inches	$8\frac{1}{4}$	$7\frac{3}{4}$	9	$8\frac{3}{4}$	$7\frac{1}{4}$	$7\frac{1}{2}$	$8\frac{1}{4}$	$7\frac{1}{2}$

   a. Draw a line plot for the data set.

   b. How much shorter is the smallest puppy than the biggest puppy?

   c. How many puppies are longer than 8 inches?

   d. How many puppies are shorter than 8 inches?

2. Sandy used this table to record how many hours she read each day.

Sandy's Reading Log

Day	Hours Spent Reading
Monday	$\frac{3}{4}$
Tuesday	$\frac{1}{2}$
Wednesday	$1\frac{1}{4}$
Thursday	$1\frac{3}{4}$
Friday	2
Saturday	$1\frac{1}{2}$
Sunday	$3\frac{1}{4}$

a. Make a line plot of the data in the table.

b. How many total hours did Sandy spend reading this week?

c. On which two days did she read more — on Saturday and Sunday or on Wednesday and Thursday? By how much more?

d. What might be some reasons to explain why Sandy read more on those two days?

Name _____

Common Core Standards Practice

4.MD.C.5a Recognize angles as geometric shapes that are formed wherever two rays share a common endpoint, and understand concepts of angle measurement: • An angle is measured with reference to a circle with its center at the common endpoint of the rays, by considering the fraction of the circular arc between the points where the two rays intersect the circle. An angle that turns through $\frac{1}{360}$ of a circle is called a "one-degree angle" and can be used to measure angles. 4.MD.C.5b Recognize angles as geometric shapes that are formed wherever two rays share a common endpoint, and understand concepts of angle measurement: • An angle that turns through n one-degree angles is said to have an angle measure of n degrees.

1. Look at the angle in the circle.

  a. What fraction of the circle is inside the angle?

  b. A circle has 360°. How can you find the measure of the angle?

  c. What is the measure of the angle?

2. Look at the angle in the circle.

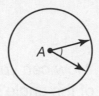

  a. What fraction of the circle is inside the angle?

  b. A circle has 360°. How can you find the measure of the angle?

  c. What is the measure of the angle?

3. Look at the angle in the circle.

  a. What fraction of the circle is inside the angle?

  b. A circle has 360°. How can you find the measure of the angle?

  c. What is the measure of the angle?

4. Look at the angle in the circle.

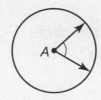

  a. What fraction of the circle is inside the angle?

  b. A circle has 360°. How can you find the measure of the angle?

  c. What is the measure of the angle?

5. Look at the angle in the circle.

   a. What fraction of the circle
      is inside the angle?

   b. A circle has 360°. How can you
      find the measure of the angle?

   c. What is the measure of
      the angle?

6. Look at the angle in the circle.

   a. What fraction of the circle
      is inside the angle?

   b. A circle has 360°. How can you
      find the measure of the angle?

   c. What is the measure of
      the angle?

7. Look at the angle in the circle.

   a. What fraction of the circle
      is inside the angle?

   b. A circle has 360°. How can you
      find the measure of the angle?

   c. What is the measure of
      the angle?

8. Look at the angle in the circle.

   a. What fraction of the circle
      is inside the angle?

   b. A circle has 360°. How can you
      find the measure of the angle?

   c. What is the measure of
      the angle?

Name _____

Common Core Standards Practice

4.MD.C.6 Measure angles in whole-number degrees using a protractor. Sketch angles of specified measure.

You will need a protractor for this lesson.

1. Use the protractor to draw an angle at point *O* that measures 75°.

2. Use the protractor to draw an angle at point O that measures 140°.

3. Use the protractor to draw an angle at point O that measures 90°.

Use the protractor to measure each angle.

4.

5.

6.

7.

8.

9.

CC 58

Name _____

Common Core Standards Practice

4.MD.C.7 Recognize angle measure as additive. When an angle is decomposed into non-overlapping parts, the angle measure of the whole is the sum of the angle measures of the parts. Solve addition and subtraction problems to find unknown angles on a diagram in real world and mathematical problems, e.g., by using an equation with a symbol for the unknown angle measure.

1. Look at the angles below.

    a. How can you find the measure of angle *RLM*?

    b. Find the measure of angle *RLM* without using a protractor. Explain how you found the measure of the angle.

2. Look at the angles below.

    a. How can you find the measure of angle *XYW*?

    b. Find the measure of angle *XYW* without using a protractor. Explain how you found the measure of the angle.

3. Two angles form where Lee Street meets Elm Street. One angle measures 31°. The two angles add together to make an angle of 180°, which is a straight line.

31°
Lee Street
Elm Street

a. Find the other angle on the diagram between the two streets. Label it *a*.

b. What is the measurement of angle *a*? Write an equation and solve.

5. Look at the angles below. The measure of angle *NMS* is twice the measure of angle *SMB*. Write an equation to find the measure of angle *NMS*. Use a letter to represent the unknown. Then solve the equation.

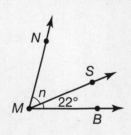
N
S
n
22°
M
B

4. In any triangle, the sum of the measures of the three angles equals 180°. In one triangle, the three angles measure 80°, 66°, and *x*. What is *x*? Write an equation and then solve it.

6. Angle *SRT* and angle *TRU* have the same measure.

S
150°
T
Q
72° x
x
R
U

a. How can you find the measure of angle *SRT*?

b. Write one or more equations to match your way.

c. What is the measure of angle *SRT*?

Name _____

Common Core Standards Practice

4.G.A.1 Draw points, lines, line segments, rays, angles (right, acute, obtuse), and perpendicular and parallel lines. Identify these in two-dimensional figures.

1. Draw an acute angle.

Explain why the angle you drew is an acute angle.

2. Circle all of the right angles in the figure shown.

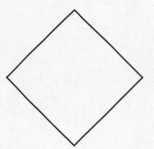

4. Does the figure shown have any perpendicular lines? Label with an X any perpendicular lines.

3. Draw a line and a line segment. Explain how a line is different from a line segment.

5. Draw an obtuse angle.

Explain why the angle you drew is an obtuse angle.

6. Draw a ray and an angle. Explain how a ray and an angle are the similar, but different.

7. Does the figure shown have any pairs of parallel lines? How do you know? If there are parallel lines, put an X on one pair.

8. Draw two lines that are perpendicular. Explain why the lines you drew are perpendicular.

9. Does the figure shown have any perpendicular lines? How do you know? If there are perpendicular lines, put an X on one pair.

Name _____

Common Core Standards Practice

4.G.A.2 Classify two-dimensional figures based on the presence or absence of parallel or perpendicular lines, or the presence or absence of angles of a specified size. Recognize right triangles as a category, and identify right triangles.

1. Draw these figures in the appropriate column. Some figures may be drawn in two columns.

At least one pair of parallel lines	No pairs of parallel lines	At least one set of perpendicular lines	No perpendicular lines

2. Using the same figures from item 1, draw them in the appropriate column. Some figures may be drawn in two columns.

At least one acute angle	At least one right angle	At least one obtuse angle

3. Draw these figures in the appropriate column. Some figures may be drawn in two columns.

At least one pair of parallel lines	No pairs of parallel lines	At least one set of perpendicular lines	No perpendicular lines

4. Using the same figures from item 1, draw them in the appropriate column. Some figures may be drawn in two columns.

At least one acute angle	At least one right angle	At least one obtuse angle

Name _____

Common Core Standards Practice

4.G.A.3 Recognize a line of symmetry for a two-dimensional figure as a line across the figure such that the figure can be folded along the line into matching parts. Identify line-symmetric figures and draw lines of symmetry.

1. Draw one or more lines of symmetry through the figure below.

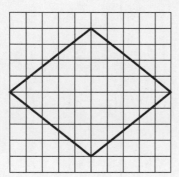

2. Draw one or more lines of symmetry through the figure below.

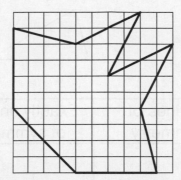

3. Draw one or more lines of symmetry through the figure below.

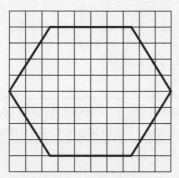

4. Draw one or more lines of symmetry through the figure below.

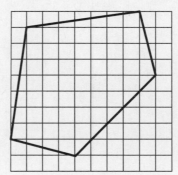

5. Determine the number of lines symmetry for each shape. Draw the shapes in the correct boxes. Some boxes may have more than one shape. Some boxes may have no shapes.

No lines of symmetry	Exactly one line of symmetry	Exactly two lines of symmetry	More than two lines of symmetry

Name _____

Practice End-of-Year Assessment

1. Use the protractor to draw an angle of 40°.
    One side of the angle is drawn for you.

2. Circle all of the fractions that are greater than $\frac{4}{9}$.

    $\frac{4}{5}$ $\frac{4}{10}$ $\frac{4}{8}$ $\frac{4}{12}$

    $\frac{4}{20}$ $\frac{4}{6}$ $\frac{4}{11}$ $\frac{4}{7}$

3. The table shows three bills that the Brock family paid in March. Find the total of the three bills.

Hockey gear	$862
Car repair	$1,055
Now carpeting	$3,293

4. Tell whether the equation below is true. Shade the model to explain your answer.

$$\frac{7}{10} \stackrel{?}{=} \frac{70}{100}$$

5. At 3:00 P.M., Ted and Bonnie both leave Hale School on their bicycles. Ted rides west $3\frac{1}{3}$ miles to his house. Bonnie rides east $3\frac{2}{3}$ miles to her house. How far do Ted and Bonnie live from each other?

6. At the school book fair, 4 times as many volunteers worked on Wednesday as on Monday. There were 16 volunteers on Wednesday.

Write an equation that you can use to find how many volunteers worked at the book fair on Monday. Use the letter M to represent the number of Monday volunteers.

7. Rectangle *ABCD* is shown below, along with the diagonal $\overline{AC}$. Which two line segments are perpendicular to each other?

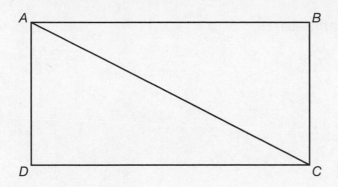

A $\overline{AC}$ and $\overline{AB}$

B $\overline{AB}$ and $\overline{DC}$

C $\overline{AD}$ and $\overline{AC}$

D $\overline{AD}$ and $\overline{DC}$

8. A marble factory produces 3,250 marbles a day. The marbles are gathered in groups of 8 and placed in a bag. How many bags of marbles does the factory produce each day? Explain how you found your answer.

9. Write an inequality comparing 45.82 and 45.79. Use the appropriate math symbol. Tell how you know which number is greater.

10. Hank's family orders three large pizzas for dinner every Friday night. Each pizza is cut into 8 equal slices. Last Friday, Hank ate two slices from each of the three pizzas.

a. Draw a model to show what Hank ate.

b. Write an equation that matches your model.

c. Did Hank eat more or less than one full pizza? Explain how you know.

11. Jake goes with his mother to the animal shelter one afternoon each week. Last week, he counted the number of cats and dogs at the shelter. He counted 7 cats and 3 times as many dogs as cats.

a. Write an equation that can be used to find the number of dogs that Jake counted. Use the letter d to represent the number of dogs.

b. How many dogs did Jake count at the shelter?

12. Find the difference. 932.4 − 540.7

13. Find a fraction that is equal to $\frac{4}{12}$. Draw models to prove that the two fractions are equivalent.

14. Write $\frac{4}{10}$ as a decimal.

15. What is 23,702 rounded to the nearest thousand? Explain your answer.

16. Triangle *ABC* is an equilateral triangle. Each angle measures 60°. What is the measure of angle *x*?

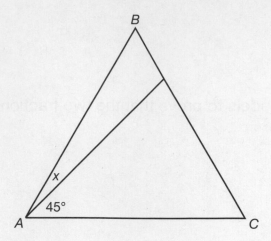

17. Find the difference.

$$7\frac{1}{4} - 3\frac{3}{4}$$

18. Hannah helps her grandfather harvest corn at his farm. She measures the length of 10 ears of corn and record the lengths in a table.

Ear of corn	1	2	3	4	5	6	7	8	9	10
Length in inches	$13\frac{1}{2}$	$14\frac{1}{4}$	$13\frac{3}{4}$	$14\frac{1}{2}$	$14\frac{1}{4}$	14	$15\frac{1}{4}$	$14\frac{1}{2}$	$14\frac{3}{4}$	$14\frac{3}{4}$

a. Make a line plot to show the lengths of the ears of corn.

b. How much longer is the longest ear of corn compared to the shortest?

c. How many ears of corn are longer than 14 inches?

19. Which of these statements about the number below is true?

233,232

A The first 2 represents a value that is 10 times greater than the second 2.

B The first 3 represents a value that is one hundred times greater than the second 3.

C The first 3 represents a value that is 10 times greater than the second 3.

D The first 2 represents a value that is one hundred times greater than the second 2.

20. Find the quotient.

2,444 ÷ 7.

21. List all of the factor pairs for the number 42.

22. Mitchell School held a food drive. Students brought in canned goods for one week. At the end of the week, all of the canned goods were brought to a food pantry. The table shows how many canned goods the students in three grades brought in.

Grade	Number of Canned Goods
Grade 3	106
Grade 4	251
Grade 5	263

How many canned goods did the students in these three grades bring in? Write an equation and solve it.

23. Today, Leela is 10 years older than her sister Amy. Her age is also 3 times Amy's age.

  a. Write an equation to compare Leela's age and Amy's age. Use the letter L to represent Leela's age and the letter A to represent Amy's age.

  b. Write another equation that uses a different operation to compare Leela's age and Amy's age. Use the letter L to represent Leela's age and the letter A to represent Amy's age.

  c. As Leela and Amy get older, which of the two equations will always be true? Explain why.

24. Write a number statement to compare the numbers 1,217 and 1,388. Explain how you know which number is greater.

25. Figure *ABCD* is a rectangle, and Point *X* is on the side of the rectangle between points *A* and *B*. A line segment connects point *X* and point *C*.

How many right angles does figure *AXCD* have?

A 0

B 1

C 2

D 4

26. Find the product of 2,386 and 4.

27. Place these fractions on the number line below.

$$\frac{5}{8}, \frac{1}{8}, \frac{7}{8}, \frac{3}{8}$$

a. Compare $\frac{3}{8}$ and $\frac{1}{8}$ by comparing them to a benchmark fraction on the number line.

b. Compare $\frac{5}{8}$ and $\frac{7}{8}$ by comparing them to a benchmark fraction on the number line.

28. Gigi says that 4,271 rounded to the nearest hundred is 4,200.

   a. Is her answer correct? Explain how you know.

   b. What should be the answer?

29. Libby and Josh bake a pie with Libby's grandmother. Libby wants to take home $\frac{1}{6}$ of the pie, while Josh wants to take home $\frac{3}{6}$ of it. How much pie will Libby's grandmother have?

   a. Draw a model to match the problem situation.

   b. Write an equation to match the model you drew.

   c. Solve the equation you wrote. How much pie will Libby's grandmother have?

30. Rina's town has voted to build a new park. The park will be 25 feet long and 15 feet wide.

   a. Draw a model of the park.

   b. What will be the area of the park?

31. Draw models to compare these fractions: $\frac{3}{5}$, $\frac{3}{4}$, and $\frac{1}{2}$.

32. Use models to compare these two decimals. Which is greater?

   0.7   0.07

33. Brian gets a weekly allowance of $10. He decides to save $3 each week from his allowance. Complete the table below to show how much he will save in 6 weeks.

Week	1	2	3	4	5	6
Savings	$3					

34. One morning, Sue milked 8 dairy goats. Each goat produced $\frac{3}{4}$ liter of milk. How much milk did Sue get from the 8 goats?

    a. Write an equation to find how much milk Sue got from the goats. Use the letter T to represent the amount of milk.

    b. Solve the equation to find T in liters.

35. Find the product.

      $5{,}087 \times 5$

36. Stan and Kayli are painting a fence. Stan paints $\frac{1}{8}$ of the fence and Kayli paints $\frac{3}{8}$ of the fence. How much of the fence do they paint together?

37. A large carton of fresh produce has a mass of 32 kilograms. What is mass in grams?

38. Find the sum.

$$\frac{7}{10} + \frac{3}{100}$$

39. The staff at Trudy's Cafe sold 104 cups of coffee on Saturday, which was 4 times as many cups as they sold on Sunday.

a. Write an equation that can be used to determine how many cups of coffee Trudy's Cafe sold on Sunday.

b. Solve the equation to find the number of cups sold on Sunday.

40. Write the expanded form of 3,062.

41. Draw lines to match the fraction with the decimal.

0.37 $\frac{3}{10}$

0.54 $\frac{5}{10}$

0.5 $\frac{54}{100}$

0.3 $\frac{37}{100}$

42. Leah wrote a 5-digit number on a piece of paper. She gave her friend Karen these clues to find the number.

What number did Leah write?

a. The 3 is in the place that is ten times greater than the place where the 5 is.

b. The 5 is in the place that is one hundred times less than the place where the 8 is.

c. The 2 is in the place that is ten times less than the place where the 5 is.

d. The 9 is in the place that is ten times greater than the place where the 8 is.

CC 81

43. Draw a line of symmetry on this image.

44. Joni's mother is an event planner, She is planning a dinner for 432 guests. The banquet room has small round tables that seat 6 guests and large round tables that seat 10 guests.

    a. How many tables will Joni's mother need if she uses the small tables? Write an equation to find the number of small tables. Use the letter *s* to represent the small tables. Then find the solution.

    b. How many tables will Joni's mother need if she uses the large tables? Write an equation to find the number of large tables. Use the letter *l* to represent the large tables.

45. Draw models to show that $\frac{2}{3} = \frac{4}{6}$.

Name _____

Performance Task 1

Camp Walkie-Talkies

Part A

The treasurer of a camp has a $1,000 budget to buy walkie-talkies for 56 campers. Each camper must have a walkie-talkie. The camp treasurer has narrowed down the choices to two models, Model A and Model B.

Each model has different prices depending on how they are ordered. The prices, including tax, for Model A and Model B are shown below.

Walkie-Talkie Model A

Box with 6 pair—$34/pair
1 pair—$42/pair

Walkie-Talkie Model B

Box with 24 pair—$33/pair
1 pair—$53/pair

1. Which model can the camp treasurer order with his $1,000 budget? Show and explain your work. Use a model to explain your calculations.

Part B

The director of the same camp wants to make sure that when the older campers go on their 6-day hike, they will be able to use the new walkie-talkies during each day of the hike. She learns that both models have 15 hours of talk time (the amount of time a person can talk without recharging batteries). She will direct the camp counselors to set a limit on the number of minutes the campers can use the walkie-talkies each day of the hike.

2. How long can each camper use his or her walkie-talkie each day if it is used for the same amount of time each day?

3. Write an equation to show how you solved the problem in Question 2. Let t = the amount of time a camper can use the walkie-talkie each day.

Name _____

Performance Task 2
Animal Shelter Volunteers
Part A

Roshanna and LeShan volunteer at their local animal shelter on Wednesdays after school. At the shelter they feed the dogs their afternoon meal according to the amounts of food given in the table below.

Other volunteers feed the dogs the same amounts in the morning. Each dog eats the same brand and type of food as the other dogs.

Dog	Amount of Dog Food per meal
Dante	$\frac{2}{3}$ cup
Shaggy	$\frac{1}{2}$ cup
Tessa	$\frac{3}{4}$ cup
Milo	$\frac{2}{3}$ cup
Sasha	$\frac{1}{2}$ cup
Bubba	$\frac{3}{4}$ cup

1. How much dog food does the shelter use each day to feed Tessa and Bubba? Use an equation and pictures of fraction models to support your answer.

2. How much dog food does the shelter use each week to feed Dante and Milo?

CC 85

Part B

Alia also volunteers at the same shelter. She feeds the cats in the shelter. The table shows the amount of food she gives to each cat each day.

Cat	Amount of Cat Food
Rascal	$\frac{5}{8}$ cup
Baggie	$\frac{1}{2}$ cup
Tabitha	$\frac{3}{4}$ cup
Tiger	$\frac{2}{3}$ cup

3. Compare the amount of food Rascal eats in a day with the amount of food Baggie eats in a day. Give two different comparisons. Show visual models to support your comparisons. Use the $>$ sign in one comparison and the $<$ sign in the other comparison.

4. Alia feeds the cats in order of the amount of cat food that they are fed. She starts with the cat who gets the least amount of food. In what order does Alia feed all of the cats?

Name _____

Practice for Common Core Assessment 2

1. Use the protractor to draw an angle of 120°. One side of the angle is drawn for you.

2. Circle all of the fractions that are less than $\frac{3}{8}$.

$\frac{3}{10}$ $\frac{3}{4}$ $\frac{3}{9}$ $\frac{3}{12}$ $\frac{3}{5}$ $\frac{3}{6}$ $\frac{3}{20}$ $\frac{3}{3}$

3. An electronic system counts all of the vehicles that cross the Adams Bridge. The chart shows the number of vehicles that crossed the bridge for three days in May.

Day	Vehicles
May 1	3409
May 2	1288
May 3	2518

What is the total number of vehicles that crossed the bridge during these three days?

4. Tell whether the equation below is true. Use models to explain your answer. $\frac{2}{10} \overset{?}{=} \frac{22}{100}$.

5. Anna and Jasmine competed in a race. Anna finished in $5\frac{1}{4}$ minutes. Jasmine finished in $4\frac{3}{4}$ minutes. How much longer was Anna running?

6. A farmer has 52 red hens, which is 4 times the number of her white hens.

Write an equation that can be used to find the number of white hens at the farm. Use W to represent the white hens.

7. In the figure below, which two lines are parallel?

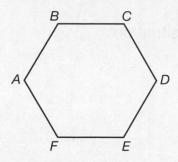

A $\overline{AB}$ and $\overline{DE}$

B $\overline{AB}$ and $\overline{CD}$

C $\overline{BC}$ and $\overline{DE}$

D $\overline{AF}$ and $\overline{DE}$

8. A truck driver wants to drive a total of 1,845 miles in 5 days. For each day's mileage to be the same, how many miles should she drive each day? Explain how you found your answer.

9. Write an inequality comparing 15.02 and 14.86. Explain how you know which number is greater.

10. A scout troop buys 4 large pizzas, each divided into 8 equal sections. The scouts eat 5 slices from each pizza.

    a. Draw a model to match the problem situation.

    b. Write an equation that matches your model.

    c. Did the scouts eat more or less than 3 whole pizzas?

11. Frieda gathered 91 red peppers from her garden, 7 times greater than the number of yellow peppers that she gathered.

    a. Write an equation that can be used to find the number of yellow peppers Frieda gathered from her garden. Use the letter y to represent the number of yellow peppers.

    b. How many yellow peppers did Frieda gather from her garden?

12. Subtract 128.7 from 300.1.

13. Find a fraction that is equal to $\frac{2}{6}$. Draw models to show that the two fractions are equivalent.

14. Write the fraction $\frac{9}{10}$ as a decimal.

15. What is 63,492 rounded to the nearest thousand? Explain your answer.

16. As shown in the diagram, angle *ABD* measures 23° and angle *DBC* measures 78°. What is the measurement of angle *ABC*?

17. Subtract $2\frac{1}{4}$ from $7\frac{3}{8}$.

18. A scientist collected some insects and measured their lengths. She recorded their lengths in a table.

Insect	A	B	C	D	E	F	G	H	I	J
Length (in.)	$\frac{1}{4}$	$\frac{1}{2}$	$\frac{1}{2}$	$\frac{1}{4}$	$\frac{1}{4}$	$\frac{1}{2}$	$\frac{3}{8}$	$\frac{1}{4}$	$\frac{3}{8}$	$\frac{1}{2}$

a. Make a line plot of the data.

b. How much longer is the longest insect than the shortest insect?

c. How many insects are longer than $\frac{1}{4}$ inch?

19. Which of these statements about the number below is true?

6,263.2

A The first 6 represents a value that is 10 times greater than the second 6.

B The first 6 represents a value that is 100 times greater than the second 6.

C The first 2 represents a value that is 100 times greater than the second 2.

D The first 2 represents a value that is 10 times greater than the second 2.

20. Find the quotient.

5,016 ÷ 9

21. List all of the factor pairs for the number 63.

22. Red Airlines has passengers board an airplane in four groups. The chart shows the number of passengers in Groups A, B, and C on Flight 12 from New York to Atlanta. The airplane can hold 135 passengers.

Passengers on Red Airlines, Flight 12

Group A	34 passengers
Group B	29 passengers
Group C	38 passengers
Group D	?

If all seats are filled, how many passengers are in Group D? Write an equation and solve it.

23. The students in Ms. Simon's class have 4 times as many dogs as fish. The students have 5 more cats than fish.

a. Write an equation to compare the number of dogs and fish that the students in Ms. Simon's class have. Use d to represent the number of dogs and f to represent the number of fish.

b. Write an equation to compare the number of cats and fish that the students in Ms. Simon's class have. Use c to represent the number of cats and f to represent the number of fish.

c. Can you write an equation that compares the number of cats and dogs that the students in Ms. Simon's class have? Explain your answer.

24. Write a number statement to compare the numbers 8,257 and 7,789. Explain how you know which number is greater.

25. Which of these triangles has one right angle?

A

B

C

D

26. What is the product of 3092 and 7?

27. Place these fractions on the number line below.

$$\frac{1}{12}, \frac{5}{12}, \frac{7}{12}, \frac{11}{12}$$

0          $\frac{1}{2}$ $\frac{2}{2}$

a. Compare $\frac{5}{12}$ and $\frac{7}{12}$ by comparing them to a benchmark fraction on the number line.

b. Compare $\frac{7}{12}$ and $\frac{11}{12}$ by comparing them to a benchmark fraction on the number line.

28. Parker says that 2,872 rounded to the nearest hundred is 2,800.

    a. Is his answer correct? Explain how you know.

    b. What should be the answer?

29. Mary and José are painting a mural on a school wall. José paints $\frac{3}{8}$ of the mural and Mary paints $\frac{2}{8}$ of the wall. How much of the wall is left to paint?

    a. Draw a model to match the problem situation.

    b. Write an equation to match the model you drew. Use x to represent the unpainted part of the wall.

    c. Solve the equation you wrote. How much of the wall is left to paint?

30. Mica's father has 48 feet of fencing. He wants to use it to put a fence around the family vegetable garden. Mica's father thinks the garden should be in the shape of a square.

    a. Draw a model of the garden.

    b. Write an equation and solve to find the length of each side.

31. Draw models to compare these fractions $\frac{7}{6}$, $\frac{7}{9}$, and 1.

32. Omar measured a distance of 1.2 meters. Sue measured a distance of 0.9 meter. Use models to compare the distances. Which distance is greater?

33. On May 1, Paula counted $2.00 in her piggy bank. She decided to add $1.50 to the bank every day, beginning the next day.

Complete the chart to show the total in the bank from May 1 to May 7.

Date	May 1	May 2	May 3	May 4	May 5	May 6	May 7
Total	$2.00						

34. Tasha lined up 9 sticks end to end. Each stick has a length of $\frac{5}{6}$ yard.

a. Write an equation for L, the total length of the 9 sticks.

b. Solve the equation to find L in yards.

35. Find the product.

2,437 × 7

CC 99

36. Deena and three of her friends are picking up trash from the beach. Each of them cleans a different part of the beach. Deena cleans $\frac{2}{5}$ of the beach. Each of her friends cleans $\frac{1}{5}$ of the beach. How much of the beach do they clean together?

37. A sack of potatoes weighs 5 pounds. How much do the potatoes weigh in ounces?

38. What is the sum of $\frac{2}{10}$ and $\frac{9}{100}$?

39. During one week at Trudy's Cafe, the staff sold 4 times as many banana muffins as chocolate chip muffins. They sold 76 banana muffins that week.

   a. Let C equal the number of chocolate chip muffins sold at the cafe. Write an equation that includes C.

   b. Solve the equation to find the number of chocolate chip muffins that they sold.

40. Write the expanded form of 7,160.

41. Draw lines to match the fraction with the decimal.

0.44 $\frac{6}{10}$

0.4 $\frac{6}{100}$

0.6 $\frac{4}{10}$

0.06 $\frac{4}{100}$

42. Many numbers can be made with the digits 9, 0, and 3. In which of the following numbers is the digit 9 in a place that is 10 times the place of the digit 3?

A 3,900

B 9,030

C 930

D 903

43. Draw two lines of symmetry on the figure shown below.

44. Myra is storing songs on a music player. Each song lasts 4 minutes, and the player can hold 232 minutes of music.

　　a. How many songs can Myra store on the music player? Write an equation to find the number of songs. Use the letter *s* to represent the songs.

　　b. Solve the equation to find the number of songs.

45. Draw two circle models to show that $\frac{2}{8} = \frac{1}{4}$.

Name _____

Performance Task 3
Studying Animals
Part A

Ms. Gregoire's students go to the Science Museum once a month. This month they are studying birds and the eggs that different kinds of bird lay. Students will explore the size of the eggs compared to the size of the adult bird.

The museum bird specialist set out eggs from 15 different kinds of birds and told the students to sort the eggs into four groups. In Group 1 are eggs that are less than 3 centimeters in length; in Group 2 are eggs that are 3 centimeters and longer but less than 6 centimeters in length; in Group 3 are eggs that are 6 centimeters and longer, but less than 9 centimeters; and in Group 4 are eggs that are 9 centimeters and longer.

Type of Bird Egg	Length of Egg (in cm)
American Crow	3.97
American Robin	2.71
Bald Eagle	7.32
Barn Owl	4.14
California Condor	10.96
Canada Goose	9.25
Common Loon	7.91
Golden Eagle	7.23
Goldfinch	1.71
Great Horned Owl	5.12
Hummingbird	1.24
King Penguin	10.73
Red-Tailed Hawk	5.97
Whooping Crane	9.55
Wild Turkey	5.14

1. Which group will have the most eggs? Which group will have the fewest? List the groups in order from fewest to most eggs.

2. Explain how you sorted the eggs into the groups.

Part B

Alfredo, the Museum bird specialist has asked Ms. Gregoire's students to help him count the number of bird eggs in his collection so he can place an order for more eggs. The table below shows how many of different bird eggs the students counted. Alfredo started to fill in the rest of the table to show how many eggs he needs and how many he needs to order to have the number he needs.

3. Complete the table for Alfredo.

Type of Bird Egg	Egg Count	Number of Eggs Needed	Number of Eggs Needed	Number of Eggs to Order
American Crow	5	3 more	8	3
American Robin	8	2 times as many	16	8
Bald Eagle	3	3 times as many		
Barn Owl	4	2 more		
California Condor	2	4 times as many		
Goldfinch	7	5 more		
Great Horned Owl	5	2 times as many		
King Penguin	4	4 more		
Red-Tailed Hawk	3	4 times as many		
Wild Turkey	8	4 more		

4. Which operations did you use to complete the table. Explain how you knew which operation to use.

Performance Task 4

Arts and Crafts Design

Part A

Mr. Jones, the art teacher at Gifford Elementary School, is having his fourth-grade classes design their own stained glass windows using geometric figures. Before designing their own windows, the students will study some design samples of stained glass. Mr. Jones has given his students the design on the right to study.

1. What are all of the different geometric shapes in the design of the window?

2. How can the different shapes be grouped? Explain why you grouped the shapes as you did.

Part B

Mr. Jones' students will make a stained glass design. Each design must have these elements:

- Parallel lines
- Perpendicular lines
- Line symmetry
- 3 different quadrilaterals
- 3 different triangles, including right triangles

3. What might one student's design look like? Draw the design inside the rectangular space below. Label in your design each of the required elements listed above.

Answers and Rubrics

Name _____

Common Core Standards Practice

4.OA.A.1 Interpret a multiplication equation as a comparison, e.g., interpret 35 = 5 × 7 as a statement that 35 is 5 times as many as 7 and 7 times as many as 5. Represent verbal statements of multiplicative comparisons as multiplication equations.

1. Which equation shows that 30 is 6 times as many as 5?

A 11 = 6 + 5
B 30 = 6 × 5
C 25 = 5 × 5
D 24 = 30 − 6

2. Which equation shows that r is 9 times as many as 6?

A $r = 9 \times 6$
B 6 × r = 9
C 6 = 9 × r
D 54 = r × 9 × 6

3. Last week, Sharon's mother ordered 60 roses for her shop. This week, she will order 5 times as many roses. How many roses will she order? Write an expression and then find the solution.

$R = 5 \times 60$

$R = 300$ roses

4. Aubrey's school has two meeting rooms. The small room seats 25 students. The large room seats three times as many students. How many students does the large room seat? Write an expression and then find the solution.

$L = 3 \times 25$

$L = 75$

5. Write a multiplication equation to show that 42 is 7 times as many as 6.

$42 = 7 \times 6$

6. Write a multiplication equation to show that 150 is s times as many as 15.

$15 \times s = 150$

CC1

page CC 1

---

7. Write an equation to find the amount that is 4 times as much as 9.

$4 \times 9 = 36$

8. Write an equation to find the amount that is 7 times as much as 8.

$7 \times 8 = 56$

9. Write an equation to show that 81 is 9 times n.

$81 = 9 \times n$

10. One building has f floors. Its taller neighbor has 3 times as many floors. The taller building has 18 floors. Write an equation for f, the number of floors in the first building.

$3 \times f = 18$

11. The students in Mrs. Aubrey's class brought in 15 cans during week 1 of the food drive. During week 2 the students brought in 4 times as many cans. How many cans did the students bring in during week 2?

60 cans

12. Joey earns $3 each time he walks the Mathers' dog. He earns twice as much when he walks the Randolphs' dog. How much does he earn when he walks the Randolphs' dog? Write an expression that models the comparison.

$6, $3 × 2

CC2

page CC 2

Name _____

Common Core Standards Practice

4.OA.A.2 Multiply or divide to solve word problems involving multiplicative comparison, e.g., by using drawings and equations with a symbol for the unknown number to represent the problem, distinguishing multiplicative comparison from additive comparison.

1. This year, the music school has 85 students. Last year it had 17 students. How many times greater is this year's number of students?

a. Write an equation for f.

$85 = 17 \times f$

b. Solve the equation you wrote.

$f = 5$; The number of students is 5 times greater.

2. Jennifer bought 12 postcards at a yard sale. Frieda bought 8 times as many postcards.

a. Write an equation that can be used to find n, the number of postcards that Frieda bought.

$12 \times 8 = n$

b. Solve the equation you wrote.

$n = 96$; Frieda bought 96 postcards.

3. At the apple orchard, Lisa picks 75 apples. Lisa picks 5 times more apples than Sharon picks.

a. Write an equation that can be solved for a, the number of apples that Sharon picks.

$75 = 5 \times a$

b. Solve the equation you wrote.

$a = 15$. Sharon picks 15 apples.

CC3

page CC 3

---

4. Janice uses 6 markers for an art project. Ivan uses 4 times as many markers as Janice.

a. Write an equation to show the number of markers m that Ivan uses.

$6 \times 4 = m$

b. Draw a model to illustrate the equation you wrote.

Check students' models.

c. Solve the equation you wrote.

$m = 24$; Ivan uses 24 markers.

5. Al sold 19 tickets to the school orchestra concert. Judy sold 3 more tickets than Al. Maria sold 3 times as many tickets as Al.

a. What operation must you use to find out how many tickets Maria sold? Explain.

Multiplication; check students' explanations.

b. Write an expression that you can use to find the number of tickets that Judy sold.

$19 + 3$

c. How many tickets did Judy sell?

Judy sold 22 tickets.

d. Write an expression that you can use to find the number of tickets that Maria sold.

19×3

e. How many tickets did Maria sell?

Maria sold 57 tickets.

CC4

page CC 4

Common Core Standards Practice

4.OA.A.3 Solve multistep word problems posed with whole numbers and having whole-number answers using the four operations, including problems in which remainders must be interpreted. Represent these problems using equations with a letter standing for the unknown quantity. Assess the reasonableness of answers using mental computation and estimation strategies including rounding.

1. George brought $94 to the shopping mall. He used the money to buy a shirt for $25, a pair of pants for $42, and 2 pairs of socks that each cost $6.

   How much money did George have after he finished shopping at the mall?

   $15

2. Nancy chopped the vegetables shown in the table, then mixed them into a salad. She divided the salad equally into 5 containers.

Broccoli	2 cups
Cauliflower	1 cup
Green peppers	2 cups
Red peppers	1 cup
Cucumbers	3 cups
Lettuce	6 cups

   How many cups of vegetables did Nancy put in each container?

   3 cups

3. At the school carnival, students sold 483 hamburgers for $4 each and 214 hot dog for $2 each.

   a. Write an equation to find how much money they took in from the sale of hamburgers. Use the letter h to represent the unknown amount. Then solve the equation.

   $$483 \times 4 = h; h = \$1932$$

   b. Write an equation to find how much money they took in from the sale of hot dogs. Use the letter d to represent the unknown amount. Then solve the equation.

   $$214 \times 2 = d; d = \$428$$

   c. How much money did they take in from the hamburgers and hot dogs?

   $2360

CC 5

page CC 5

---

4. The Walters family bought 3 ham sandwiches and 4 fruit cups for lunch. Each sandwich cost $4 and each fruit cup cost $2. How much did the family spend on lunch?

   The family spent $20.

5. Volunteers at the park will plant 150 marigold plants and 60 petunia plants. They will plant 5 rows of petunias and twice as many rows of marigolds.

   a. How many rows of marigolds will the volunteers plant?

   10

   b. How many petunias will they plant in each row?

   12

6. Mr. Chen wants to buy 27 blue pens and 35 red pens. The pens are sold in packages of 8.

   a. How many packages of blue pens must he buy? Write an equation using the letter b for the unknown amount. Then solve the equation.

   $27 \div 8 = b; b = 3$ R3. He will need 4 packages of blue pens.

   b. How many packages of red pens will Mr. Chen buy? Write an equation and use the letter r for the unknown amount. Then solve the equation.

   $35 \div 8 = r; r = 4$ R3. He will need 5 packages of red pens.

   c. One package of pens costs $2. How much will Mr. Chen spend on pens?

   $18

CC 6

page CC 6

Common Core Standards Practice

4.OA.B.4 Find all factor pairs for a whole number in the range 1–100. Recognize that a whole number is a multiple of each of its factors. Determine whether a given whole number in the range 1–100 is a multiple of a given one-digit number. Determine whether a given whole number in the range 1–100 is prime or composite.

1. Which of these are prime numbers? Circle all of the numbers that are prime.

   ⑰   �37   38
   45   57   ㊾
   63   84   ㊴

2. Which of these numbers are composite? Circle all of the numbers that are composite.

   2   5   ⑨
   19   �33   ㊺
   53   ㊾   �91

3. Which of these numbers is a multiple of 8? Circle all of the numbers that are multiples of 8.

   2   3   4
   ⑯   20   ㉜
   36   ㊽   54
   ㊌

4. Which set of numbers are all factors of 50?

   Ⓐ 1, 2, 5, 10, 25, 50
   B 1, 2, 8, 12, 24, 50
   C 1, 4, 5, 10, 12, 50
   D 1, 4, 5, 9, 10, 50

5. Is 39 a prime or composite number? Explain how you know.

   Composite. 39 has more than two factors. The factors of 39 are 1, 3, 13, and 39.

6. List four multiples of 9.

   Sample answer: 27, 36, 45, 81

CC 7

page CC 7

---

7. Write all of the factor pairs for 28.

   1, 28; 2, 14; 4, 7

8. The number 36 is a multiple of several numbers. List all of them.

   1, 2, 3, 4, 6, 9, 12, 18, 36

9. Which of these numbers are prime? Which are composite? Put an X on the prime numbers. Circle the composite numbers. In the space below, write the factors of each number that you identified as composite.

   ✗   ✗   ✗   �33   ✗
   ✗   ㊞63   ✗   ✗   ㉝93

   Only 33, 63, and 93 are composite; the others are prime. Factors of 33: 1, 3, 11, 33 Factors of 63: 1, 3, 7, 9, 63 Factors of 93: 1, 3, 31, 93

10. What is the only even prime number? Explain how you know.

    The only even prime is 2. All other even numbers have 2 as a factor.

11. Answer each question. Explain how you know.

    Is 81 a multiple of 3?
    Yes. $81 = 3 \times 3 \times 3 \times 3$
    Is 46 a multiple of 4?
    No. $46 = 2 \times 23$
    Is 55 a multiple of 7?
    No. $55 = 5 \times 11$
    Is 72 a multiple of 9?
    Yes. $72 = 9 \times 8$
    Is 45 a multiple of 6?
    No. $45 = 3 \times 3 \times 5$

CC 8

page CC 8

Common Core Standards Practice

4.OA.C.5 Generate a number or shape pattern that follows a given rule. Identify apparent features of the pattern that were not explicit in the rule itself.

1. Continue the pattern below. Use the rule, "Add 4."

4, __8__ , __12__ , __16__ , __20__ , __24__

What do you notice about the digits in the ones place?
They are even numbers.

2. Draw shapes to continue the pattern. Use the rule, "Add one side to the shape."

3. Continue the pattern below. Use the rule, "Divide by 2."

96, __48__ , __24__ , __12__ , __6__ , __3__

4. a. Continue the pattern below. Use the rule, "Move the dot around the square."

b. Look closely. What pattern do you see that is not mentioned in the rule?
Every fourth square, the dot appears in the same place.

page CC 9

---

5. a. Complete the number sequence below by using the rule, "Subtract 5."

50, __45__ __40__ __35__ __30__ __25__ __20__

b. What do you notice about the digits in the ones place?
They alternate between 0 and 5.

6. a. Complete the number sequence below by using the rule, "Add 2."

3, __5__ , __7__ , __9__ , __11__ , __13__ , __15__

b. What do you notice about the numbers in the pattern?
All of the numbers are odd. An odd number plus 2 is always another odd number.

7. Complete the pattern by using the rule, "Add a dot to the square."

page CC 10

Common Core Standards Practice

4.NBT.A.1 Recognize that in a multi-digit whole number, a digit in one place represents ten times what it represents in the place to its right.

1. Jonah wrote a 5-digit number on a piece of paper. He gave his friend Marbey these clues to find the number.

  a. The 4 is in the place that is ten times greater than the place where the 2 is.

  b. The 2 is in the place that is one hundred times less than the place where the 5 is.

  c. The 6 is in the place that is ten times less than the place where the 2 is.

  d. The 1 is in the place that is ten times greater than the place where the 5 is.

What is the number? **15,426**

2. Which of these statements is true about the number shown.

169,961

(A) The first 9 represents a value ten times greater than the second 9.

B The first 9 represents a value one hundred times greater than the second 9.

C The first 6 represents a value ten times greater than the second 6.

D The first 6 represents a value one hundred times greater than the second 6.

3. Look at the number below.

75,575

  a. How many times does the digit 5 appear in the number?
  3

  b. How do the values of the digit 5 differ in the number?
  Sample answer: The first 5 is in the thousands place, the second is in the hundreds place, and the third is in the ones place.

  c. How much greater is the value of the first 5 compared to the value of the second 5?
  ten times greater

  d. How much greater is the value of the second 5 compared to the value of the third 5?
  one hundred times

page CC 11

---

4. Which of these statements is true about the number shown?

78,409

A The 7 represents a value that is 10 times greater than the 4.

B The 4 represents a value that is 10 times greater than the 9.

(C) The 8 represents a value that is 10 times greater than the 4.

D The 8 represents a value that is 2 times greater than the 4.

5. Minah gives the following clues about a 5-digit number.

  a. The 8 is in a place that is 100 times greater than the place of the 2.

  b. The 2 is in a place that is 100 times greater than the place of the 0.

  c. The 3 is in a place that is 10 times less than the place of the 8.

  d. The 5 is in a place that is 100 times less than the place of the 3.

What is the number?
83,250

6. Look at the number below.

38,108

  a. How many times does the digit 8 appear in the number?
  2

  b. How do the values of the digit 8 differ in the number?
  Sample answer: The first 8 is in the thousands place, the second is in the ones place.

  c. How much greater is the value of the first 8 compared to the value of the second 8?
  1,000 times greater

  d. Write a number with the same digits, but make the place of the first 8 be 10 times the place of the second 8.
  Possible answer: 38,810

page CC 12

page CC 13

Name _____

Common Core Standards Practice

4.NBT.A.2 Read and write multi-digit whole numbers using base-ten numerals, number names, and expanded form. Compare two multi-digit numbers based on meanings of the digits in each place, using >, =, and < symbols to record the results of comparisons.

1. What is 3,106 in expanded form?

   (A) 3,000 + 100 + 6
   B 3,000 + 10 + 6
   C 3,000 + 6
   D 3,000 + 100 + 60

2. Thirty-five thousand, four hundred seventeen people attended a county fair. What is this number in standard form?

   A 35,174
   (B) 35,417
   C 35,470
   D 35,471

3. What is 9,000 + 800 + 30 + 1 in standard form?

   A 9,031
   B 9,138
   C 9,381
   (D) 9,831

4. Which symbol should replace the circle to make the number sentence true?

   438 ◯ 400 + 30 + 8

   A <
   B ≠
   (C) =
   D >

5. Write 4,230 in expanded form.

   4,000 + 200 + 30

6. Write a number sentence to compare 89,723 and 89,372. Use the < symbol.

   89,372 < 89,723

   Explain how you know which number is greater.

   Each number begins with the same two digits, and the third digit is greater in 89,723.

page CC 14

7. A group of 246 people attend the school play. Write this number in words.

   two hundred forty-six

8. Write twenty-seven thousand, six hundred twelve in expanded form.

   20,000 + 7,000 + 600 + 10 + 2

9. Dali sold one hundred fourteen tickets for the fundraiser. Sharon sold 141. Who sold more tickets? Write a number sentence to show your answer.

   Sharon sold more.
   114 < 141

10. Write 3,406 in words and in expanded form.

    three thousand, four hundred six
    3,000 + 400 + 6

11. Write a number sentence that compares 58,219 and 58,231.

    58,231 > 58,219, or 58,219 < 58,231

    Explain how you knew which symbol to use.

    The numbers are the same until the tens place, in which 3 is greater than 1.

12. What symbol should replace the circle to make the number sentence true?

    1,998 ◯ two thousand fourteen

    <

    Explain how you knew which symbol to use.

    Sample answer: the first number has 1 in the thousands place, the second number has 2 in the thousands place; 2,000 is greater than 1,000.

page CC 15

Name _____

Common Core Standards Practice

4.NBT.A.3 Use place value understanding to round multi-digit whole numbers to any place.

1. What is 192 rounded to the nearest ten?

   A 100
   B 180
   (C) 190
   D 200

2. Which number rounds to 5,600 when it is rounded to the nearest hundred?

   A 5,674
   (B) 5,637
   C 5,549
   D 5,512

3. The school talent show raised $2,914. What is this amount rounded to the nearest thousand and to the nearest hundred?

   nearest thousand: $3,000
   nearest hundred: $2,900

4. What is 6,708 rounded to the nearest ten?

   6,710

5. On Thursday, 45 students walked to school. What is this number rounded to the nearest ten?

   50

6. Aisha thinks that 1,275 rounded to the nearest hundred is 1,200 because "2 is less than 5."

   a. What might be Aisha's misunderstanding about rounding?
   Sample answer: Aisha is looking at the incorrect place to round.

   b. Help Aisha correct her misunderstanding by explaining rounding.
   Sample answer. Aisha needs to look at the digit in the place to the right of the number being rounded and not at the number being rounded.

page CC 16

7. The population of Centerville is 89,582. What is the population rounded to the nearest thousand?

   (A) 90,000
   B 89,600
   C 89,500
   D 89,000

8. A newspaper reported that about 27,000 people attended a major league baseball game. If the actual attendance was rounded to the nearest thousand, how many people could have attended the game?

   A 27,942
   B 27,610
   (C) 26,789
   D 26,495

9. Write a number that would round to 5,000 when it is rounded to the nearest thousand.
   Sample answer: 5,341

10. Write two numbers that round to 150 when they are rounded to the nearest ten.
    Sample answer: 147, 152

11. The attendance at an amusement park during the month of July was 174,383. What is the attendance rounded to the nearest thousand?
    174,000

12. Ken says that 9,138 rounded to the nearest thousand is 9,100 because "3 is less than 5."

    a. What might be Ken's misunderstanding about rounding?
    Sample answer: Ken rounded to the nearest hundred, not the nearest thousand.

    b. Help Ken correct his misunderstanding.
    Sample answer. Ken needs to round to the correct place value. The number 9,138 rounded to the nearest thousand is 9,000.

Name _____

Common Core Standards Practice

4.NBT.B.4 Fluently add and subtract multi-digit whole numbers using the standard algorithm.

1. Use the information in the table to answer each question below.

City	Population (2010)
Gulfport, MS	67,793
Redlands, CO	8,685
Rocky River, OH	20,213

a. In 2000, the population of Gulfport, MS, was 71,127. How many more people lived in Gulfport, MS, in 2000 than in 2010?

3,334

b. In 2010, how many more people lived in Rocky River, OH, than in Redlands, CO?

11,528

c. In 2010, what was the total population of the three cities listed in the table?

96,691

2. Find the sum.
```
  4,068
+ 2,291
```
6,359

3. Find the difference.
```
  500,000
− 184,875
```
315,125

page CC 17

---

4. Students at the Lincoln Elementary School are selling tickets to the school spring fair. The third graders have sold 1,673 tickets. The fourth graders have sold 3,098 tickets. What is the total number of tickets the students in both classes have sold?

A 1,425
B 4,671
Ⓒ 4,771
D 5,771

5. A cowgirl spends $995 on a used trail saddle. She also spends $360 on new saddlebags. How much does she spend in all?

A $1,365
Ⓑ $1,355
C $1,255
D $635

6. Miles is 1,196 weeks old. His younger sister Abby is 468 weeks old.

a. Write and solve an equation to show the difference in their ages in weeks.

1,196 − 468 = 728; 728 weeks

b. Write and solve an equation to show their total ages.

1,196 + 468 = 1,664; 1,664 weeks

page CC 18

Name _____

Common Core Standards Practice

4.NBT.B.5 Multiply a whole number of up to four digits by a one-digit whole number, and multiply two two-digit numbers, using strategies based on place value and the properties of operations. Illustrate and explain the calculation by using equations, rectangular arrays, and/or area models.

1. Find the product.
```
 2,056
×    9
```
18,504

2. Find the product.
```
  89
× 27
```
2,403

3. Hannah is helping her grandmother make a quilt. Each row will have 16 squares. There will be 14 rows.

a. Draw a model of the quilt.

b. How many squares will Hannah and her grandmother need to make?

224 squares

page CC 19

---

4. Juan bakes and sells dog treats at the farmers market. He always fits 12 treats on a cookie sheet. On Saturday, he bakes 8 batches of dog treats.

a. Draw an array to match the problem situation.

Check students' arrays.

b. Write an equation to show how many dog treats Juan bakes.

12 × 8 = ?

c. Solve the equation you wrote.

96 treats

5. An Olympic-sized swimming pool is 50 meters long and 25 meters wide.

a. Draw a model to show the area of an Olympic-sized pool.

b. Write an equation to show the area of an Olympic-sized pool.

50 × 25 = ?

c. Solve the equation you wrote.

1,250 square meters

6. Principal Watts walks 5 miles every day. How many miles does he walk in 1 year, or 365 days? Write and solve an equation.

5 × 365 = ?; 1,825 miles

page CC 20

Common Core Standards Practice

4.NBT.B.6 Find whole-number quotients and remainders with up to four-digit dividends and one-digit divisors, using strategies based on place value, the properties of operations, and/or the relationship between multiplication and division. Illustrate and explain the calculation by using equations, rectangular arrays, and/or area models.

1. Find the quotient.

   486 ÷ 3 **162**

2. Find the quotient.

   1,250 ÷ 7 **178 R4**

3. Aaron raises chickens. He sells chicken eggs by the dozen. On Friday, Aaron sold 96 eggs. How many dozen eggs did Aaron sell?

   a. Draw a rectangular array to model the problem situation.

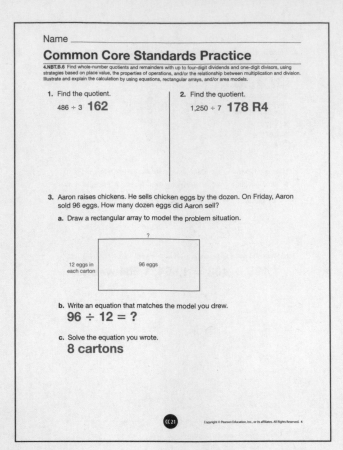

   b. Write an equation that matches the model you drew.

   96 ÷ 12 = ?

   c. Solve the equation you wrote.

   8 cartons

page CC 21

---

4. Claire helps at her mother's flower shop. This week, her mother received a shipment of 250 sunflowers. Claire put them in bundles of 8 flowers. How many bundles did she make? Did she have any bundles with fewer than 8 sunflowers? If so, how many more sunflowers would she need to complete the bundle?

   31 bundles, yes, she had one bundle with fewer than 8 sunflowers. She would need 6 more flowers to make a full bundle.

5. A tailor sews 8 buttons on each jacket he makes. He has 220 buttons. On how many jackets can he sew buttons?

   220 ÷ 8 = 27 R4; he can make 27 jackets.

6. Green Valley City Park has an area of 6,557 square feet. The length of the park is 83 feet.

   a. Draw a model to show Green Valley City Park.

   Length: 83 ft

   Width ?

   Area = 6,557 square ft

   b. Write and solve an equation to show how to find the width of the park.

   6,557 ÷ 83 = ?; ? = 79 ft

page CC 22

Common Core Standards Practice

4.NF.A.1 Explain why a fraction $\frac{a}{b}$ is equivalent to a fraction $\frac{(n \times a)}{(n \times b)}$ by using visual fraction models, with attention to how the number and size of the parts differ even though the two fractions themselves are the same size. Use this principle to recognize and generate equivalent fractions.

1. Stella and Brian each heat up a small pizza. Stella cuts her pizza into 4 equal slices. Brian cuts his pizza into 8 equal parts.

   a. Draw models of Stella's pizza and Brian's pizza.

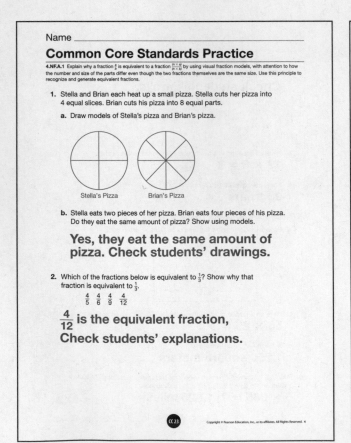

   Stella's Pizza   Brian's Pizza

   b. Stella eats two pieces of her pizza. Brian eats four pieces of his pizza. Do they eat the same amount of pizza? Show using models.

   Yes, they eat the same amount of pizza. Check students' drawings.

2. Which of the fractions below is equivalent to $\frac{1}{3}$? Show why that fraction is equivalent to $\frac{1}{3}$.

   $\frac{4}{5}$ $\frac{4}{6}$ $\frac{4}{9}$ $\frac{4}{12}$

   $\frac{4}{12}$ is the equivalent fraction, Check students' explanations.

page CC 23

---

3. Which two models show equivalent fractions? Explain how you know.

   A   B   C

   Models A and C show equivalent fractions; $\frac{3}{5} = \frac{6}{10}$

4. Four students draw a design for a class flag. Each flag is black and white. Shown below are four designs. Which designs have the same fractions of black and white? Explain how you know.

   Madison's design   Kyle's design

   Jason's design   Lina's design

   Sample answer: Madison's and Lina's designs have the same fractions of black and white. Each have two equal parts, one part is black and one part is white.

page CC 24

page CC 25

Name _____

Common Core Standards Practice

4.NF.A.2 Compare two fractions with different numerators and different denominators, e.g., by creating common denominators or numerators, or by comparing to a benchmark fraction such as ½. Recognize that comparisons are valid only when the two fractions refer to the same whole. Record the results of comparisons with symbols >, =, or <, and justify the conclusions, e.g., by using a visual fraction model.

1. Which fraction is less than $\frac{5}{8}$?

A $\frac{7}{8}$

B $\frac{6}{8}$

C $\frac{5}{6}$

Ⓓ $\frac{4}{8}$

2. Which fraction is greater than $\frac{1}{7}$?

Ⓐ $\frac{1}{5}$

B $\frac{1}{8}$

C $\frac{1}{9}$

D $\frac{1}{10}$

3. A kitchen floor has green, yellow, and white tiles. Of those tiles, $\frac{2}{5}$ are green and $\frac{2}{10}$ are yellow. Are there more green tiles than yellow tiles? Explain how you know.

There are more green tiles. A whole divided into 5 sections has fewer sections than a whole divided into 10 sections, so each $\frac{1}{5}$ section is larger than each $\frac{1}{10}$ section.

4. Barry got a small sandwich for lunch and ate $\frac{1}{2}$ of his sandwich. Jonah got a large sandwich and ate $\frac{1}{2}$ of his sandwich. Did Jonah and Barry eat the same amount for lunch? Explain how you know.

No, they didn't, even though they both ate $\frac{1}{2}$ of their sandwiches. Jonah ate more because his sandwich was larger.

CC 25

---

page CC 26

5. Place these fractions on the number line below. Then complete the inequalities.

$\frac{2}{5}$ $\frac{1}{4}$ $\frac{4}{6}$ $\frac{5}{8}$

a. $\frac{2}{5}$ $\underline{<}$ $\frac{1}{2}$ and $\frac{4}{6}$ $\underline{>}$ $\frac{1}{2}$ so $\frac{2}{5}$ $\underline{<}$ $\frac{4}{6}$.

b. $\frac{5}{8}$ $\underline{>}$ $\frac{1}{2}$ and $\frac{1}{4}$ $\underline{<}$ $\frac{1}{2}$ so $\frac{5}{8}$ $\underline{>}$ $\frac{1}{4}$.

c. $\frac{4}{6}$ $\underline{>}$ $\frac{1}{2}$ and $\frac{4}{6}$ $\underline{<}$ $\frac{2}{2}$ and $\frac{5}{8}$ $\underline{>}$ $\frac{1}{2}$ and $\frac{5}{8}$ $\underline{<}$ $\frac{2}{2}$ and $\frac{5}{8}$ $\underline{<}$ $\frac{4}{6}$.

6. Tell which fraction is greater: $\frac{6}{8}$ $\underline{>}$ $\frac{6}{10}$. Write < or >.

Draw models of fraction strips to prove your answer.

7. Inez compared the fractions $\frac{1}{5}$ and $\frac{1}{3}$. She said, "I compared the denominators. Because 5 is greater than 3, $\frac{1}{5}$ is greater than $\frac{1}{3}$."

Is Inez correct? Explain your answer.

Possible response: I don't agree. A larger denominator means that there are a greater number of parts, so each part is smaller. If the numerators are the same, that means that the smaller denominator is a larger fraction.

CC 26

---

page CC 27

Name _____

Common Core Standards Practice

4.NF.B.3a Understand addition and subtraction of fractions as joining and separating parts referring to the same whole.

1. Nan drew a model to show the addition of two fractions.

Write an equation to match Nate's model.

$\frac{1}{4} + \frac{2}{4} = \frac{3}{4}$

2. Amy runs $\frac{2}{5}$ of a mile. Then she walks another $\frac{2}{5}$ of a mile.

a. How far does Amy run and walk? Use the number line to model the problem.

b. Write and solve an equation to match your model.

$\frac{2}{5} + \frac{2}{5} = \frac{4}{5}$

3. Mr. Kopek cuts a pie into 8 equal pieces. He eats two pieces and his son eats three pieces.

a. What fraction of the pie do Mr. Kopek and his son eat? Draw a model to match the problem.

b. Write an equation to match your model.

$\frac{2}{8} + \frac{3}{8} = \frac{5}{8}$

CC 27

---

page CC 28

4. Kyle draws a model to show the subtraction of two fractions.

Write an equation to match the model.

$\frac{5}{6} - \frac{2}{6} = \frac{3}{6}$

5. Fen bought $\frac{3}{4}$ yard of cloth. She used $\frac{1}{4}$ yard to make a napkin. How much cloth does she have left?

$\frac{2}{4}$

6. In spring, Toni divided her vegetable garden into 3 equal sections. She planted beans in one section, corn in the second section, and squash in the third section. One day in autumn, Toni harvested all the beans and squash.

a. Draw a model to match the problem situation.

Check students' models.

b. What fraction of the garden has Toni not yet harvested?

$\frac{3}{3} - \frac{2}{3} = \frac{1}{3}$

CC 28

Page CC 29

Name _____

Common Core Standards Practice

4.NF.B.3b Decompose a fraction into a sum of fractions with the same denominator in more than one way, recording each decomposition by an equation. Justify decompositions, e.g., by using a visual fraction model.

1. Jiro thinks of a fraction. He decomposes the fraction into three fractions shown below.

$\frac{1}{6} + \frac{1}{6} + \frac{3}{6}$ $\qquad$ $\frac{5}{6}$

What fraction is Jiro thinking of? Tell how you know.

2. Chloe uses fractions strips to show $\frac{7}{8}$ as the sum of fractions.

Draw another way to show $\frac{7}{8}$ as the sum of fractions.

Check students' models.

Write an equation to match your models.

Answers may vary. Possible response:

$\frac{5}{8} + \frac{2}{8} = \frac{7}{8}$ or $\frac{1}{8} + \frac{1}{8} + \frac{1}{8} + \frac{4}{8} = \frac{7}{8}$

CC 29   Copyright © Pearson Education, Inc., or its affiliates. All Rights Reserved. 4

Page CC 30

3. Write $\frac{7}{8}$ as the sum of unit fractions.

$\frac{1}{8} + \frac{1}{8} + \frac{1}{8} + \frac{1}{8} + \frac{1}{8} + \frac{1}{8} + \frac{1}{8} = \frac{7}{8}$

4. Write $1\frac{2}{3}$ as the sum of two fractions that have the same denominator.

Possible answer: $\frac{3}{3} + \frac{2}{3} = \frac{5}{3} = 1\frac{2}{3}$

Write $1\frac{2}{3}$ as the sum of a whole number and two fractions that have the same denominator.

$1 + \frac{1}{3} + \frac{1}{3} = 1\frac{2}{3}$

5. To show a fraction, George placed these fraction strips on his desk.

What fraction does his model show? Write the fraction as a sum of the fractions in the model.

$\frac{2}{10} + \frac{3}{10} + \frac{3}{10} = \frac{8}{10}$

CC 30   Copyright © Pearson Education, Inc., or its affiliates. All Rights Reserved. 4

Page CC 31

Name _____

Common Core Standards Practice

4.NF.B.3c Add and subtract mixed numbers with like denominators, e.g., by replacing each mixed number with an equivalent fraction, and/or by using properties of operations and the relationship between addition and subtraction.

Find the sum or difference. Explain how you found the sum or difference.

1. $3\frac{1}{4} + 2\frac{3}{4} =$ $5\frac{4}{4} = 6$

2. $4\frac{5}{6} - 3\frac{1}{6} =$ $1\frac{4}{6}$

3. Sherri swam $2\frac{5}{8}$ miles on Monday. She swam $1\frac{1}{8}$ miles on Wednesday.

a. How many miles did Sherri swim on Monday and Wednesday?

$3\frac{6}{8}$ miles

b. How many more miles did Sherri swim on Monday than on Wednesday? Write an equation and solve.

$2\frac{5}{8} - 1\frac{1}{8} = 1\frac{4}{8}$ miles

4. What is the sum of $10\frac{3}{5}$ and $6\frac{3}{5}$?

A 4

B $\frac{166}{5}$

C $16\frac{1}{5}$

Ⓓ $17\frac{1}{5}$

CC 31   Copyright © Pearson Education, Inc., or its affiliates. All Rights Reserved. 4

Page CC 32

5. What addition sentence does the model show?

$\frac{1\frac{1}{4}}{} + \frac{2\frac{3}{4}}{} = \frac{3\frac{4}{4} \text{ or } 4}{}$

6. Subtract. Explain how you found the difference.

$9\frac{3}{3}$
$-1\frac{2}{3}$

$7\frac{2}{3}$ **Check students' explanations.**

7. Check your answer to problem 6 by adding. Explain how you found your work.

$8\frac{4}{3} = 9\frac{1}{3}$ **Check students' explanations.**

CC 32   Copyright © Pearson Education, Inc., or its affiliates. All Rights Reserved. 4

page CC 33

Name _____

Common Core Standards Practice

4.NF.B.3d Solve word problems involving addition and subtraction of fractions referring to the same whole and having like denominators, e.g., by using visual fraction models and equations to represent the problem.

1. Georgia is mixing colors to paint a door. She pours $\frac{3}{8}$ cup of red paint into a can. Then she adds $\frac{2}{8}$ cup of blue paint to the can.

   a. How much paint is in the can? Write an equation.

   $$\frac{3}{8} + \frac{2}{8} = ?$$

   b. Solve your equation.

   $$\frac{3}{8} + \frac{2}{8} = \frac{5}{8}; \frac{5}{8} \text{ cup}$$

2. A piece of tape is $\frac{10}{12}$ inch long. Diego cuts off $\frac{5}{12}$ inch of the piece of tape.

   a. Use the number line to show a model of the problem.

   b. How much tape is left?

   $$\frac{5}{12} \text{ inch}$$

page CC 34

3. Erika lives on a farm. Her father uses $\frac{1}{8}$ of the farm land to grow soy beans and $\frac{3}{8}$ of the farm land to grow corn. The rest of the farm land is used as grazing land for cattle.

   a. Draw a model to match the problem.

Corn	Corn	Corn	Soy beans
Cattle	Cattle	Cattle	Cattle

   b. What fraction of the farm land is used to grow crops (corn and soy beans)?

   $$\frac{4}{8}$$

   c. What fraction of the farm land is used for cattle grazing?

   $$\frac{4}{8}$$

4. Jamal spends $\frac{3}{4}$ of an hour writing a short story. Then he spends $\frac{1}{4}$ of an hour revising the story. How much longer does Jamal spend writing than revising? Write and solve an equation.

   $$\frac{3}{4} - \frac{1}{4} = \frac{2}{4}; \frac{2}{4} \text{ hour}$$

page CC 35

Name _____

Common Core Standards Practice

4.NF.B.4a Understand a fraction $\frac{a}{b}$ as a multiple of $\frac{1}{b}$.

1.

   a. How many sections are shaded? ___ **3**

   b. What fraction of the model is shaded? ___ $\frac{3}{4}$

2.

   a. How many sections are shaded? ___ **2**

   b. What fraction of the model is shaded? ___ $\frac{2}{5}$

3. Shade parts of the circle to model the fraction $\frac{5}{6}$.

   How many parts did you shade? ___ **6**

4. Draw a model to show three equal parts of a whole. Then shade parts of the model to show $\frac{2}{3}$.

   Two of the three pieces of the figure should be shaded.

   How many parts did you shade? ___ **2**

page CC 36

5. Julie divides a board into 8 equal pieces. Draw a model to show Julie's board.

   a. Julie paints $\frac{4}{8}$ of the board. How many pieces of the board does she paint? ___ **4**

   b. How many pieces of the board are not painted? ___ **4**

   What fraction of the board do the unpainted pieces represent? ___ $\frac{4}{8}$

6. Jorge divides a circle into 12 equal slices. Draw a model to match.

   a. Jorge cuts out $\frac{3}{12}$ of the circle. How many slices of the circle does he cut out? ___ **3**

   b. How many slices of the circle are left? ___ **9**

   What fraction of the circle remains? ___ $\frac{9}{12}$

Page CC 37

Name _____

Common Core Standards Practice

4.NF.B.4b Understand a multiple of $\frac{a}{b}$ as a multiple of $\frac{1}{b}$, and use this understanding to multiply a fraction by a whole number.

1. What is $4 \times \frac{3}{4}$? Explain how you know.

Sample answer: $4 \times \frac{3}{4}$ is the same as $4 \times 3 \times \frac{1}{4} = \frac{12}{4} = 3$

2. What is $2 \times \frac{3}{8}$? Explain how you know.

$\frac{6}{8}$, or $\frac{3}{4}$ Check students' answers.
Sample answer: $2 \times \frac{3}{8}$ is the same as $2 \times 3 \times \frac{1}{8} = 6 \times \frac{1}{8} = \frac{6}{8}$

3. What is $5 \times \frac{2}{3}$? Explain how you know.

$\frac{10}{3}$, or $3\frac{1}{3}$ Check students' answers.
Sample answer: $5 \times \frac{2}{3}$ is the same as $5 \times 2 \times \frac{1}{3} = 10 \times \frac{1}{3} = \frac{10}{3}$

page CC 37

Page CC 38

4. What is $4 \times \frac{2}{3}$?

$\frac{8}{3}$, or $2\frac{2}{3}$

5. Find $\frac{5}{6} \times 7$.

$\frac{35}{6}$, or $5\frac{5}{6}$

6. Multiply $\frac{3}{7}$ and 5.

$\frac{15}{7}$, or $2\frac{1}{7}$

7. Multiply $\frac{4}{7}$ and 2.

$\frac{8}{7}$, or $1\frac{1}{7}$

8. What is $3 \times \frac{4}{3}$?

4

9. What is $5 \times \frac{8}{9}$?

$\frac{40}{9}$, or $4\frac{4}{9}$

10. Multiply $\frac{3}{5}$ and 6.

$\frac{18}{5}$, or $3\frac{3}{5}$

11. Multiply $\frac{2}{9}$ and 7.

$\frac{14}{9}$, or $1\frac{5}{9}$

page CC 38

Page CC 39

Name _____

Common Core Standards Practice

4.NF.B.4c Solve word problems involving multiplication of a fraction by a whole number, e.g., by using visual fraction models and equations to represent the problem.

1. Fern is helping her mother make decorations for a family gathering. Fern is putting lace around napkins. For each napkin, Fern needs $\frac{3}{5}$ yard of lace. Fern will put the lace on 10 napkins.

a. Use a number line model to show the problem.

Check students' number lines.

b. Write an equation to match the model. Use the letter l to represent the amount of lace that Fern will need.

$l = 10 \times \frac{3}{5}$

c. How many yards of lace will Fern need? Explain your answer.

She will need $\frac{30}{5}$, or 6 yards of lace.

2. Mindy wants to paint her room. Her mother tells her that she will need $\frac{2}{3}$ gallon of paint for each of the 4 walls. How much paint will she need?

a. Draw a model to match the problem.

Check students' drawings.

b. Write an equation to match the model. Use the letter p to represent the amount of paint Mindy will need.

$4 \times \frac{2}{3} = p$

c. How many gallons of paint will Mindy need to buy? Explain your answer.

3 gallons. Mindy needs $2\frac{2}{3}$ gallons of paint, so she will need to buy 3 gallons.

page CC 39

Page CC 40

3. Vicki has a vegetable garden. She spends $\frac{3}{4}$ hour in her vegetable garden each weekend. How many hours will she spend in her garden over the 12 weeks of summer?

a. Use a number line model to show the problem.

Check students' drawings.

b. Write an equation to match the model. Use the letter h to represent the number of hours that Vicki will spend in her garden.

$12 \times \frac{3}{4} = h$

c. How many hours will Vicki spend in the garden? Explain your answer.

She will spend 9 hours in her garden.
$12 \times \frac{3}{4} = \frac{36}{4}$

4. Frank plays in a soccer league. At each practice, he drinks $\frac{3}{5}$ gallon of sports drink. He practices 5 days a week. How many gallons of sports drink does his mother need to buy each week?

She needs to buy 3 gallons of sports drink each week.

page CC 40

page CC 41

Common Core Standards Practice

4.NF.C.5 Express a fraction with denominator 10 as an equivalent fraction with denominator 100, and use this technique to add two fractions with respective denominators 10 and 100.

1. For each of these fractions, write the equivalent fraction with a denominator of 100.

$\frac{4}{10} = \frac{40}{100}$ $\frac{7}{10} = \frac{70}{100}$

$\frac{2}{10} = \frac{20}{100}$ $\frac{9}{10} = \frac{90}{100}$

$\frac{18}{10} = \frac{180}{100}$ $\frac{26}{10} = \frac{260}{100}$

2. Find the sums.

a. $\frac{4}{10} + \frac{3}{100} = \frac{40}{100} + \frac{3}{100} = \frac{43}{100}$

b. $\frac{7}{10} + \frac{2}{100} = \frac{70}{100} + \frac{2}{100} = \frac{72}{100}$

c. $\frac{9}{10} + \frac{3}{100} = \frac{90}{100} + \frac{3}{100} = \frac{93}{100}$

d. $\frac{1}{100} + \frac{5}{10} = \frac{1}{100} + \frac{50}{100} = \frac{51}{100}$

e. $\frac{6}{100} + \frac{8}{10} = \frac{6}{100} + \frac{80}{100} = \frac{86}{100}$

page CC 42

Find the sums.

3. $\frac{5}{10} + \frac{2}{100} = \frac{50}{100} + \frac{2}{100} = \frac{52}{100}$

4. $\frac{7}{100} + \frac{2}{10} = \frac{7}{100} + \frac{20}{100} = \frac{27}{100}$

5. $\frac{8}{10} + \frac{3}{100} = \frac{80}{100} + \frac{3}{100} = \frac{83}{100}$

6. $\frac{4}{100} + \frac{3}{10} = \frac{4}{100} + \frac{30}{100} = \frac{34}{100}$

7. $\frac{6}{100} + \frac{1}{10} = \frac{6}{100} + \frac{10}{100} = \frac{16}{100}$

8. $\frac{36}{10} + \frac{8}{100} = \frac{360}{100} + \frac{8}{100} = \frac{368}{100}$

9. $\frac{11}{10} + \frac{7}{100} = \frac{110}{100} + \frac{7}{100} = \frac{117}{100}$

10. $\frac{5}{100} + \frac{2}{10} = \frac{5}{100} + \frac{20}{100} = \frac{25}{100}$

page CC 43

Common Core Standards Practice

4.NF.C.6 Use decimal notation for fractions with denominators 10 or 100.

1. Which is the decimal form of $\frac{4}{10}$?
   - (A) 0.4
   - B 4.0
   - C 0.04
   - D 0.44

2. Which fraction equals 0.29?
   - A $\frac{2}{9}$
   - B $\frac{2}{10}$
   - (C) $\frac{29}{100}$
   - D $\frac{29}{10}$

3. Write these fractions in decimal form.

$\frac{2}{10} = 0.2$ $\frac{5}{10} = 0.5$

$\frac{22}{100} = 0.22$ $\frac{78}{100} = 0.78$

$\frac{45}{100} = 0.45$ $\frac{92}{100} = 0.92$

4. Write these decimals as fractions. Use denominators of either 10 or 100.

$0.3 = \frac{3}{10}$ $0.18 = \frac{18}{100}$

$0.73 = \frac{73}{100}$ $0.8 = \frac{8}{10}$

$0.48 = \frac{48}{100}$ $0.67 = \frac{67}{100}$

page CC 44

5. The number line shows tenths from 0 to 1.

a. Write decimals to complete the number line.

b. Below the number line, add leaders and labels for these three numbers: 0.68, 0.25, and 0.82.

6. The number line shows tenths from 0 to 1.

What decimals are shown by the short lines with letters? If you are not sure, write your best estimate.

Line A: **0.2**

Line D: **0.9**

Line C: **0.65**

Line D: **0.42**

Why is it difficult to identify lines C and D exactly?

These lines are between two tenths. We don't know exactly how many hundredths they are.

page CC 45

Name _____

Common Core Standards Practice

4.NF.C.7 Compare two decimals to hundredths by reasoning about their size. Recognize that comparisons are valid only when the two decimals refer to the same whole. Record the results of comparisons with the symbols >, =, or <, and justify the conclusions, e.g., by using a visual model.

1. Plot these two decimals on the number line below.

   0.43   0.39

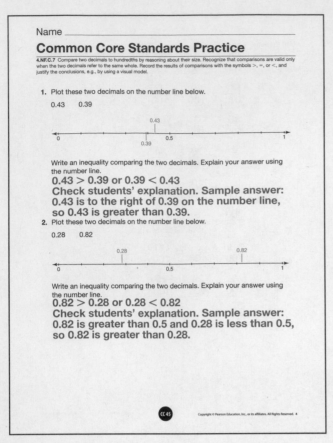

   Write an inequality comparing the two decimals. Explain your answer using the number line.
   0.43 > 0.39 or 0.39 < 0.43
   Check students' explanation. Sample answer: 0.43 is to the right of 0.39 on the number line, so 0.43 is greater than 0.39.

2. Plot these two decimals on the number line below.

   0.28   0.82

   Write an inequality comparing the two decimals. Explain your answer using the number line.
   0.82 > 0.28 or 0.28 < 0.82
   Check students' explanation. Sample answer: 0.82 is greater than 0.5 and 0.28 is less than 0.5, so 0.82 is greater than 0.28.

page CC 46

3. The baseball team started the game with two one-liter bottles of water. At the end of the game, the first bottle had 0.3 liters left and the second had 0.4 liters left.

   Draw a model to show the amount of water left in each bottle after the game.
   Check students' drawings.

   Out of which liter bottle did more player take water? the first or the second?
   Players took more water from the first bottle because there was less water left.

4. Simon and Danielle are on the baseball team. Last season, 0.15 of Simon's hits were home runs, and 0.15 of Danielle's hits were also home runs.

   a. Can you tell whether Simon and Danielle hit the same number of home runs?
   No. They may have had different numbers of hits. Whoever had more hits also had more home runs.

   b. Frank is also on the baseball team. Of his hits last season, 0.19 were home runs. Can you tell if he hit more home runs than Simon or Danielle? Explain.
   No, you cannot tell this. We don't know how many hits each player had.

5. Draw a decimal square to represent 0.33 and 0.27.

   Which is greater?
   0.27 < **0.33**

page CC 47

Name _____

Common Core Standards Practice

4.MD.A.1 Know relative sizes of measurement units within one system of units including km, m, cm; kg, g; lb, oz.; l, ml; hr, min, sec. Within a single system of measurement, express measurements in a larger unit in terms of a smaller unit. Record measurement equivalents in a two-column table.

1. A distance of 5 kilometers (km) is the same as how many meters (m)?

   A 50 m

   B 500 m

   Ⓒ 5,000 m

   D 50,000 m

2. A movie lasts 3 hours. How many minutes is this?

   A 30 minutes

   B 60 minutes

   C 120 minutes

   Ⓓ 180 minutes

3. Change each of these measurements into a smaller unit.

   7 kilograms into grams   **7,000 grams**

   5 pounds into ounces   **80 ounces**

   12 meters into centimeters   **1,200 centimeters**

   6 hours into minutes   **360 minutes**

   9 minutes into seconds   **540 seconds**

   2 pound into ounces   **32 ounces**

   4 yards into feet   **12 feet**

page CC 48

4. Decide whether each equation is true or false. If the statement is false, then write the corrected equation on the line to the right.

   4 kilometers = 4,000 meters   **true**

   10 pounds = 80 ounces   **false, 160 ounces**

   2 minutes = 90 seconds   **false, 120 seconds**

   15 liters = 0.15 milliliters   **false, 1,500 milliliters**

   3 hours = 180 minutes   **true**

   10 minutes = 300 seconds   **false, 600 seconds**

   17 kilograms = 1,700 grams   **false, 17,000 grams**

   7 meters = 700 centimeters   **true**

5. Frieda worked on her homework last night for 120 minutes. How many hours did she spend on her homework last night?
   2 hours

6. A scientist measures 5 liters of water in a beaker. How many milliliters of water did the scientist measure in the beaker?
   5,000 mL

7. How many seconds are in 1 hour? Explain how you know.
   There are 3,600 seconds in one hour. 1 hour equals 60 minutes and 1 minutes equals 60 seconds. To find the number of seconds in an hour, I multiply 60 by 60.

Common Core Standards Practice

4.MD.A.2 Use the four operations to solve word problems involving distances, intervals of time, liquid volumes, masses of objects, and money, including problems involving simple fractions or decimals, and problems that require expressing measurements given in a larger unit in terms of a smaller unit. Represent measurement quantities using diagrams such as number line diagrams that feature a measurement scale.

1. Martha and her family went to the seashore for a week-long vacation. For 5 days of their vacation, they rode bicycles around the area. The table below shows how far they rode each day.

Day	Miles
Monday	5
Tuesday	7
Wednesday	5
Thursday	8
Friday	5

a. How many miles did they ride during their week-long vacation?

30 miles

b. What was the difference between the longest and the shortest ride?

3 miles

c. Martha wanted to ride an average of 7 miles a day during the family vacation. To find the average, she took the total number of miles they rode and divided it by the 5 days. What did she find? Did she make her goal?

The average is 6 miles.

She did not meet her goal.

2. A scientist is carrying out an experiment. She measures 30 milliliters of liquid and pours it into a 100-milliliter beaker. Later, she adds another 25 milliliters of liquid to the beaker. How much more liquid can the scientist add to the beaker?

45 mL

3. Micah and his father did some laundry at the laundromat. To wash a load costs $2 and to dry a load costs another $2. Micah and his father washed and dried 4 loads of laundry. They also had to buy 4 packets of detergent for $1 per packet.

How much did Micah and his father spend to do their laundry?

$20

4. During the rainy season, the height of a river increases 70 centimeters a day. After how many days will the river increase a total of 3.5 meters?

3.5 m × 100 cm/m = 350 cm

350 cm ÷ 70 cm/day = 5 days

The increase will occur in 5 days.

CC 49

page CC 49

---

5. Jeremiah is making a care package for his sister who is away at college. He can send up to 5 pounds for a flat rate of $12.95. He puts some items in the box and then weighs it. It weighs $2\frac{3}{8}$ pounds. He has more items he would like to send. What else can he add to the box to be as close to 5 pounds without going over? What is the weight of the box with the additional items?

Item	Weight
2 small boxes of dark chocolate truffles	$1\frac{2}{8}$ pound per box
3 packets of candied fruit	$\frac{6}{8}$ pound per packet
2 packet of hair clips	$\frac{1}{8}$ pound per packet
1 small bottle of body lotion	$\frac{5}{8}$ pound per bottle

Answers may vary. Sample answer: He can add the two small boxes of dark chocolate truffles. The weight of the box would be $4\frac{7}{8}$ pounds.

6. a. Sam has a piggy bank full of quarters, dimes, nickels, and pennies. Describe two ways he could make $0.78 using only two kinds of coins.
Two of the following:
3 quarters + 3 pennies = (3 × 0.25) + (3 × 0.01) = $0.78
15 nickels + 3 pennies = (15 × 0.05) + (3 × 0.01) = $0.78
7 dimes + 8 pennies = (7 × 0.10) + (8 × 0.01) = $0.78

b. Which coin must be used in both ways?
pennies

7. Naomi stops every 600 meters as she walks a distance of 2.4 kilometers. How many stops does she make?
2.4 km = 2.4 × 1,000 m/km = 2,400 m
2,400 ÷ 600 = 4
She makes 4 stops.

8. At Hogan Airport, an airplane takes off every 12 minutes. How many airplanes take off in 5 hours?
5 h × 60 min/h = 300 min
300 ÷ 12 = 25
25 airplanes take off in 5 hours.

CC 50

page CC 50

Common Core Standards Practice

4.MD.A.3 Apply the area and perimeter formulas for rectangles in real world and mathematical problems.

1. Teresa measures the dimensions of her math book. It is 28 centimeters long and 21 centimeters wide. How can Teresa find the perimeter of her math book?

Sample answer: She can add the length and the width and then multiply by 2.

3. The area of a rectangular bedroom is 240 square feet. If the length of the bedroom is 16 feet, what is the width?
The width is 15 feet.

5. A rectangular piece of construction paper is 11 inches long and 0 inches wide. How could it be cut to make a rectangle that has an area of 32 square inches?
Sample answer: Measure 4 inches along the length. Then cut a rectangle that is 4 inches by 8 inches.

2. Ted is helping his father plant their vegetable garden this year. They will put a fence around the garden. Ted measures the length of the garden, which is 6 feet. His father tells him that the width is twice the length. How much fencing do Ted and his father need to buy to enclose the garden?

 A 36 feet
B 24 feet
C 12 feet
D 6 feet

4. The model below shows the floor plan of a room. What is the area of the room? Explain how you found your answer.

5 ft
5 ft
9 ft
3 ft
4 ft
2 ft

Area = (9 × 5) − (4 × 3) =
45 − 12 = 33
The area is 33 ft².

CC 51

page CC 51

---

6. Tasha is decorating a rectangular bulletin board by putting ribbon around its outer edge. The bulletin board is 14 inches wide and 18 inches tall. How many inches of ribbon does she need?

Perimeter = 2L + 2W

= (2 × 14) + (2 × 18) = 64

She needs 64 inches of ribbon.

7. Janice walked around two sides of a square park. The perimeter of the park is 1,200 yards. How many yards did Janice walk? Explain your answer.

One side of the park is
300 yards, so Janice walked
600 yards.

8. Joey's playhouse has a perimeter of 28 feet. What could be the dimensions of the playhouse? Draw a model and label the length and width. Show that the dimensions equal a perimeter of 28 feet.
Sample answer: Check students' models. The length and width could each be 7 feet. 4 × 7 = 28

9. Roger just got a new puppy for his birthday. He and his mother will build a fence around an area in the backyard for the puppy to play in. The play area will be 24 square feet. What dimensions could the play area be? Which dimensions would require the least amount of fencing?
The dimensions could be
4 × 6, 2 × 12, or 3 × 8. The
4 × 6 area would require
the least amount of fencing
because it has the smallest
perimeter (20 feet).

CC 52

page CC 52

Common Core Standards Practice

4.MD.B.4 Make a line plot to display a data set of measurements in fractions of a unit (½, ¼, ⅛). Solve problems involving addition and subtraction of fractions by using information presented in line plots.

1. Ryan's dog just had a litter of 8 puppies. His mother measured the length each of the puppies. The table below shows their lengths in inches.

Puppy	1	2	3	4	5	6	7	8
Length in inches	$8\frac{1}{4}$	$7\frac{3}{4}$	9	$8\frac{3}{4}$	$7\frac{1}{4}$	$7\frac{1}{2}$	$8\frac{1}{4}$	$7\frac{1}{2}$

a. Draw a line plot for the data set.

b. How much shorter is the smallest puppy than the biggest puppy?

$1\frac{3}{4}$ inches

c. How many puppies are longer than 8 inches?

4 puppies

d. How many puppies are shorter than 8 inches?

4 puppies

page CC 53

---

2. Sandy used this table to record how many hours she read each day.

Sandy's Reading Log

Day	Hours Spent Reading
Monday	$\frac{3}{4}$
Tuesday	$\frac{1}{2}$
Wednesday	$1\frac{1}{4}$
Thursday	$1\frac{3}{4}$
Friday	2
Saturday	$1\frac{1}{2}$
Sunday	$3\frac{1}{4}$

a. Make a line plot of the data in the table.

b. How many total hours did Sandy spend reading this week?

She spent 11 hours reading.

c. On which two days did she read more — on Saturday and Sunday or on Wednesday and Thursday? By how much more?

Saturday and Sunday; $1\frac{3}{4}$ hours more.

d. What might be some reasons to explain why Sandy read more on those two days?

Sample answer: Saturday and Sunday are weekend days when Sandy does not go to school, so she has more free time.

page CC 54

Common Core Standards Practice

4.MD.C.5a Recognize angles as geometric shapes that are formed wherever two rays share a common endpoint, and understand concepts of angle measurement: • An angle is measured with reference to a circle with its center at the common endpoint of the rays, by considering the fraction of the circular arc between the points where the two rays intersect the circle. An angle that turns through $\frac{1}{360}$ of a circle is called a "one-degree angle" and can be used to measure angles. 4.MD.C.5b Recognize angles as geometric shapes that are formed wherever two rays share a common endpoint, and understand concepts of angle measurement: • An angle that turns through n one-degree angles is said to have an angle measure of n degrees.

1. Look at the angle in the circle.

a. What fraction of the circle is inside the angle? $\frac{1}{4}$

b. A circle has 360°. How can you find the measure of the angle?

multiply 360 by $\frac{1}{4}$ or divide 360 by 4

c. What is the measure of the angle? **90°**

2. Look at the angle in the circle.

a. What fraction of the circle is inside the angle? $\frac{1}{8}$

b. A circle has 360°. How can you find the measure of the angle?

multiply 360 by $\frac{1}{8}$ or divide 360 by 8

c. What is the measure of the angle? **45°**

3. Look at the angle in the circle.

a. What fraction of the circle is inside the angle? $\frac{1}{3}$

b. A circle has 360°. How can you find the measure of the angle?

multiply 360 by $\frac{1}{3}$ or divide 360 by 3

c. What is the measure of the angle? **120°**

4. Look at the angle in the circle.

a. What fraction of the circle is inside the angle? $\frac{1}{5}$

b. A circle has 360°. How can you find the measure of the angle?

multiply 360 by $\frac{1}{5}$ or divide 360 by 5

c. What is the measure of the angle? **72°**

page CC 55

---

5. Look at the angle in the circle.

a. What fraction of the circle is inside the angle? $\frac{1}{4}$

b. A circle has 360°. How can you find the measure of the angle?

multiply 360 by $\frac{1}{4}$ or divide 360 by 4

c. What is the measure of the angle? **90°**

6. Look at the angle in the circle.

a. What fraction of the circle is inside the angle? $\frac{1}{8}$

b. A circle has 360°. How can you find the measure of the angle?

multiply 360 by $\frac{1}{8}$ or divide 360 by 8

c. What is the measure of the angle? **45°**

7. Look at the angle in the circle.

a. What fraction of the circle is inside the angle? $\frac{1}{2}$

b. A circle has 360°. How can you find the measure of the angle?

multiply 360 by $\frac{1}{2}$ or divide 360 by 2

c. What is the measure of the angle? **180°**

8. Look at the angle in the circle.

a. What fraction of the circle is inside the angle? $\frac{1}{6}$

b. A circle has 360°. How can you find the measure of the angle?

multiply 360 by $\frac{1}{6}$ or divide 360 by 6

c. What is the measure of the angle? **60°**

page CC 56

Common Core Standards Practice

4.MD.C.6 Measure angles in whole-number degrees using a protractor. Sketch angles of specified measure.

You will need a protractor for this lesson.

1. Use the protractor to draw an angle at point *O* that measures 75°.

2. Use the protractor to draw an angle at point *O* that measures 140°.

3. Use the protractor to draw an angle at point *O* that measures 90°.

page CC 57

Use the protractor to measure each angle.

4. **31°**

5. **172°**

6. **115°**

7. **90°**

8. **68°**

9. **148°**

page CC 58

Common Core Standards Practice

4.MD.C.7 Recognize angle measure as additive. When an angle is decomposed into non-overlapping parts, the angle measure of the whole is the sum of the angle measures of the parts. Solve addition and subtraction problems to find unknown angles on a diagram in real world and mathematical problems, e.g., by using an equation with a symbol for the unknown angle measure.

1. Look at the angles below.

a. How can you find the measure of angle *RLM*?

Answers may vary. Sample answer: Measure with a protractor, add angle *RLA* and angle *ALM*.

b. Find the measure of angle *RLM* without using a protractor. Explain how you found the measure of the angle.

120°. I added the measures of the two angles.

2. Look at the angles below.

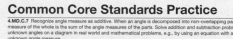

a. How can you find the measure of angle *XYW*?

Answers may vary. Sample answer: Measure with a protractor, subtract measure of angle *WYZ* from the measure of angle *XYZ*.

b. Find the measure of angle *XYW* without using a protractor. Explain how you found the measure of the angle.

58°. I subtracted the measure of angle *WYX* from the measure of angle *XYZ*.

page CC 59

---

3. Two angles form where Lee Street meets Elm Street. One angle measures 31°. The two angles add together to make an angle of 180°, which is a straight line.

a. Find the other angle on the diagram between the two streets. Label it *a*.

b. What is the measurement of angle *a*? Write an equation and solve.

$$a + 31° = 180°$$
$$a = 149°$$

5. Look at the angles below. The measure of angle *NMS* is twice the measure of angle *SMB*. Write an equation to find the measure of angle *NMS*. Use a letter to represent the unknown. Then solve the equation.

$$n = 2 \times 22°$$
$$n = 44°$$

4. In any triangle, the sum of the three angles equals 180°. In one triangle, the three angles measure 80°, 66°, and *x*. What is *x*? Write an equation and then solve it.

$$80° + 66° + x = 180°$$
$$x = 34°$$

6. Angle *SRT* and angle *TRU* have the same measure.

a. How can you find the measure of angle *SRT*?

Sample answer: subtract 72 from 150, then divide the answer by 2.

b. Write one or more equations to match your way.

Sample answer: 150 − 72 = 78; 78 ÷ 2 = 39

c. What is the measure of angle *SRT*?

39

page CC 60

page CC 61

Name _____

Common Core Standards Practice

4.G.A.1 Draw points, lines, line segments, rays, angles (right, acute, obtuse), and perpendicular and parallel lines. Identify these in two-dimensional figures.

1. Draw an acute angle.

   Explain why the angle you drew is an acute angle.
   Sample answer: The angle is less than a right angle.

2. Circle all of the right angles in the figure shown.

3. Draw a line and a line segment. Explain how a line is different from a line segment.
   Check students' drawing. A line continues on in both directions with no ending; a line segment is part of a line It has two end points.

4. Does the figure shown have any perpendicular lines? Label with an X any perpendicular lines.

5. Draw an obtuse angle.

   Explain why the angle you drew is an obtuse angle.
   Sample answer: The angle is greater than a right angle.

page CC 62

6. Draw a ray and an angle. Explain how a ray and an angle are the similar, but different.
   Check students' drawings. Sample answer: a ray is a line with one end point. An angle is made up of two rays.

7. Does the figure shown have any pairs of parallel lines? How do you know? If there are parallel lines, put an X on one pair.

   Check students' answers. Sample answer: The figure has three pairs of parallel lines.

8. Draw two lines that are perpendicular. Explain why the lines you drew are perpendicular.
   Check students' drawings. Sample answer: the lines are perpendicular because they form a right angle where they intersect.

9. Does the figure shown have any perpendicular lines? How do you know? If there are perpendicular lines, put an X on one pair.

   There are no perpendicular lines. None of the lines form a right angle

page CC 63

Name _____

Common Core Standards Practice

4.G.A.2 Classify two-dimensional figures based on the presence or absence of parallel or perpendicular lines, or the presence or absence of angles of a specified size. Recognize right triangles as a category, and identify right triangles.

1. Draw these figures in the appropriate column. Some figures may be drawn in two columns.

At least one pair of parallel lines	No pairs of parallel lines	At least one set of perpendicular lines	No perpendicular lines

2. Using the same figures from item 1, draw them in the appropriate column. Some figures may be drawn in two columns.

At least one acute angle	At least one right angle	At least one obtuse angle

page CC 64

3. Draw these figures in the appropriate column. Some figures may be drawn in two columns.

At least one pair of parallel lines	No pairs of parallel lines	At least one set of perpendicular lines	No perpendicular lines

4. Using the same figures from item 1, draw them in the appropriate column. Some figures may be drawn in two columns.

At least one acute angle	At least one right angle	At least one obtuse angle

Common Core Standards Practice

4.G.A.3 Recognize a line of symmetry for a two-dimensional figure as a line across the figure such that the figure can be folded along the line into matching parts. Identify line-symmetric figures and draw lines of symmetry.

1. Draw one or more lines of symmetry through the figure below.

2. Draw one or more lines of symmetry through the figure below.

3. Draw one or more lines of symmetry through the figure below.

4. Draw one or more lines of symmetry through the figure below.

page CC 65

---

5. Determine the number of lines symmetry for each shape. Draw the shapes in the correct boxes. Some boxes may have more than one shape. Some boxes may have no shapes.

No lines of symmetry	Exactly one line of symmetry	Exactly two lines of symmetry	More than two lines of symmetry

page CC 66

Practice End-of-Year Assessment

1. Use the protractor to draw an angle of 40°. One side of the angle is drawn for you.

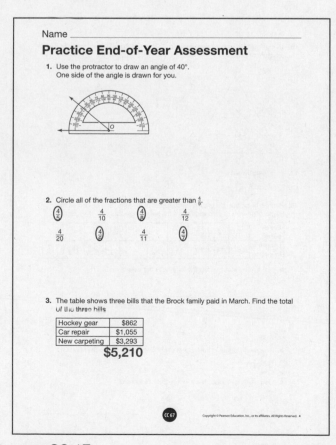

2. Circle all of the fractions that are greater than $\frac{4}{9}$.

$\frac{4}{5}$ $\frac{4}{10}$ $\frac{4}{8}$ $\frac{4}{12}$

$\frac{4}{20}$ $\frac{4}{6}$ $\frac{4}{11}$ $\frac{4}{7}$

3. The table shows three bills that the Brock family paid in March. Find the total of the three bills.

Hockey gear	$862
Car repair	$1,055
New carpeting	$3,293

$5,210

page CC 67

---

4. Tell whether the equation below is true. Shade the model to explain your answer.

$\frac{7}{10} \overset{?}{=} \frac{70}{100}$

Yes, the two are equal.

5. At 3:00 P.M., Ted and Bonnie both leave Hale School on their bicycles. Ted rides west $3\frac{1}{3}$ miles to his house. Bonnie rides east $3\frac{2}{3}$ miles to her house. How far do Ted and Bonnie live from each other?

7 miles

6. At the school book fair, 4 times as many volunteers worked on Wednesday as on Monday. There were 16 volunteers on Wednesday.

Write an equation that you can use to find how many volunteers worked at the book fair on Monday. Use the letter *M* to represent the number of Monday volunteers.

Possible equation: $16 = 4 \times M$

page CC 68

page CC 69

7. Rectangle *ABCD* is shown below, along with the diagonal $\overline{AC}$. Which two line segments are perpendicular to each other?

- A $\overline{AC}$ and $\overline{AB}$
- B $\overline{AB}$ and $\overline{DC}$
- C $\overline{AD}$ and $\overline{AC}$
- Ⓓ $\overline{AD}$ and $\overline{DC}$

8. A marble factory produces 3,250 marbles a day. The marbles are gathered in groups of 8 and placed in a bag. How many bags of marbles does the factory produce each day? Explain how you found your answer.

406 bags; Check students' explanations.

9. Write an inequality comparing 45.82 and 45.79. Use the appropriate math symbol. Tell how you know which number is greater.

45.82 > 45.79; Check students' explanations.

page CC 70

10. Hank's family orders three large pizzas for dinner every Friday night. Each pizza is cut into 8 equal slices. Last Friday, Hank ate two slices from each of the three pizzas.

   a. Draw a model to show what Hank ate.

   b. Write an equation that matches your model.

   $$3 \times \frac{2}{8} = ?$$

   c. Did Hank eat more or less than one full pizza? Explain how you know.

   He ate less than a full pizza. A full pizza is $\frac{8}{8}$ and Hank ate $\frac{6}{8}$ of a pizza. $\frac{6}{8}$ is less than $\frac{8}{8}$

11. Jake goes with his mother to the animal shelter one afternoon each week. Last week, he counted the number of cats and dogs at the shelter. He counted 7 cats and 3 times as many dogs as cats.

   a. Write an equation that can be used to find the number of dogs that Jake counted. Use the letter *d* to represent the number of dogs.

   $$7 \times 3 = d$$

   b. How many dogs did Jake count at the shelter?

   21

page CC 71

12. Find the difference. 932.4 − 540.7

   391.7

13. Find a fraction that is equal to $\frac{4}{12}$. Draw models to prove that the two fractions are equivalent.

   Check students answers.
   Accept any equivalent fraction

14. Write $\frac{4}{10}$ as a decimal.

   0.4

15. What is 23,702 rounded to the nearest thousand? Explain your answer.

   24,000; Check students' explanations.

page CC 72

16. Triangle *ABC* is an equilateral triangle. Each angle measures 60°. What is the measure of angle *x*?

   15°

17. Find the difference.

   $7\frac{1}{4} - 3\frac{3}{4}$ $\mathbf{3\frac{1}{2}}$

18. Hannah helps her grandfather harvest corn at his farm. She measures the length of 10 ears of corn and record the lengths in a table.

Ear of corn	1	2	3	4	5	6	7	8	9	10
Length in inches	$13\frac{1}{2}$	$14\frac{1}{4}$	$13\frac{3}{4}$	$14\frac{1}{2}$	$14\frac{1}{4}$	14	$15\frac{1}{4}$	$14\frac{1}{2}$	$14\frac{3}{4}$	$14\frac{3}{4}$

   a. Make a line plot to show the lengths of the ears of corn.

   b. How much longer is the longest ear of corn compared to the shortest?

   $\mathbf{1\frac{3}{4}}$ **in.**

   c. How many ears of corn are longer than 14 inches?

   7

19. Which of these statements about the number below is true?

233,232

   A The first 2 represents a value that is 10 times greater than the second 2.
   B The first 3 represents a value that is one hundred times greater than the second 3.
   Ⓒ The first 3 represents a value that is 10 times greater than the second 3.
   D The first 2 represents a value that is one hundred times greater than the second 2.

20. Find the quotient.

2,444 ÷ 7.

349 R1

21. List all of the factor pairs for the number 42.

1 × 42; 2 × 21; 3 × 14; 6 × 7

page CC 73

22. Mitchell School held a food drive. Students brought in canned goods for one week. At the end of the week, all of the canned goods were brought to a food pantry. The table shows how many canned goods the students in three grades brought in.

Grade	Number of Canned Goods
Grade 3	106
Grade 4	251
Grade 5	263

How many canned goods did the students in these three grades bring in? Write an equation and solve it.

106 + 251 + 263 = ?

? = 620

23. Today, Leela is 10 years older than her sister Amy. Her age is also 3 times Amy's age.

   a. Write an equation to compare Leela's age and Amy's age. Use the letter L to represent Leela's age and the letter A to represent Amy's age.

$L = A + 10$

   b. Write another equation that uses a different operation to compare Leela's age and Amy's age. Use the letter L to represent Leela's age and the letter A to represent Amy's age.

$L = 3 \times A$

   c. As Leela and Amy get older, which of the two equations will always be true? Explain why.

Leela will always be 10 years older than Amy, so the equation $L = A + 10$ will always be true.

page CC 74

24. Write a number statement to compare the numbers 1,217 and 1,388. Explain how you know which number is greater.

1,388 > 1,217

Check students' explanations.

25. Figure *ABCD* is a rectangle, and Point *X* is on the side of the rectangle between points *A* and *B*. A line segment connects point *X* and point *C*.

How many right angles does figure *AXCD* have?

   A 0
   B 1
   Ⓒ 2
   D 4

page CC 75

26. Find the product of 2,386 and 4.

9,544

27. Place these fractions on the number line below.

$\frac{5}{8}, \frac{1}{8}, \frac{7}{8}, \frac{3}{8}$

   a. Compare $\frac{3}{8}$ and $\frac{1}{8}$ by comparing them to a benchmark fraction on the number line.

$\frac{3}{8}$ is greater than $\frac{1}{4}$ and $\frac{1}{8}$ is less than $\frac{1}{4}$ and so $\frac{3}{8}$ is greater than $\frac{1}{8}$

   b. Compare $\frac{5}{8}$ and $\frac{7}{8}$ by comparing them to a benchmark fraction on the number line.

$\frac{5}{8}$ is less than $\frac{3}{4}$ and $\frac{7}{8}$ is greater than $\frac{3}{4}$ and so $\frac{5}{8}$ is less than $\frac{7}{8}$

page CC 76

28. Gigi says that 4,271 rounded to the nearest hundred is 4,200.

    a. Is her answer correct? Explain how you know.

No. Sample explanation: The digit to the right of the hundreds place (tens place) is greater than 5, so she should round up the digit in the hundreds place.

    b. What should be the answer?

4,300

29. Libby and Josh bake a pie with Libby's grandmother. Libby wants to take home $\frac{1}{6}$ of the pie, while Josh wants to take home $\frac{3}{6}$ of it. How much pie will Libby's grandmother have?

    a. Draw a model to match the problem situation.

    b. Write an equation to match the model you drew.

$$\frac{1}{6} + \frac{3}{6} + x = \frac{6}{6}$$

    c. Solve the equation you wrote. How much pie will Libby's grandmother have?

$$\frac{4}{6}$$

page CC 77

---

30. Rina's town has voted to build a new park. The park will be 25 feet long and 15 feet wide.

    a. Draw a model of the park.

    b. What will be the area of the park?

375 square feet.

31. Draw models to compare these fractions: $\frac{3}{5}$, $\frac{3}{4}$, and $\frac{1}{2}$.

$\frac{1}{5}$	$\frac{1}{5}$	$\frac{1}{5}$	$\frac{1}{5}$	$\frac{1}{5}$
$\frac{1}{4}$	$\frac{1}{4}$	$\frac{1}{4}$	$\frac{1}{4}$	
$\frac{1}{2}$		$\frac{1}{2}$		

32. Use models to compare these two decimals. Which is greater?

    0.7   0.07

0.7 is greater. Check students' models.

page CC 78

---

33. Brian gets a weekly allowance of $10. He decides to save $3 each week from his allowance. Complete the table below to show how much he will save in 6 weeks.

Week	1	2	3	4	5	6
Savings	$3					

Week	1	2	3	4	5	6
Savings	$3	$6	$9	$12	$15	$18

34. One morning, Sue milked 8 dairy goats. Each goat produced $\frac{3}{4}$ liter of milk. How much milk did Sue get from the 8 goats?

    a. Write an equation to find how much milk Sue got from the goats. Use the letter T to represent the amount of milk.

$$T = 8 \times \frac{3}{4}$$

    b. Solve the equation to find T in liters.

$$T = 8 \times \frac{3}{4}$$
$$T = \frac{8 \times 3}{4}$$
$$T = \frac{24}{4} = 6$$

The goats produced 6 liters of milk.

35. Find the product.

    $5{,}087 \times 5$

25,435

page CC 79

---

36. Stan and Kayli are painting a fence. Stan paints $\frac{1}{8}$ of the fence and Kayli paints $\frac{3}{8}$ of the fence. How much of the fence do they paint together?

$$\frac{1}{8} + \frac{3}{8} = \frac{4}{8}$$

37. A large carton of fresh produce has a mass of 32 kilograms. What is mass in grams?

$$32 \text{ kilograms} \times 1{,}000 \, \frac{\text{grams}}{\text{kilograms}} = 32{,}000 \text{ grams}$$

38. Find the sum.

    $\frac{7}{10} + \frac{3}{100}$

$$\frac{73}{100}$$

39. The staff at Trudy's Cafe sold 104 cups of coffee on Saturday, which was 4 times as many cups as they sold on Sunday.

    a. Write an equation that can be used to determine how many cups of coffee Trudy's Cafe sold on Sunday.

$$104 = 4 \times S$$

    b. Solve the equation to find the number of cups sold on Sunday.

$$\frac{104}{4} = S; \; S = 26 \text{ cups}$$

page CC 80

40. Write the expanded form of 3,062.

$$3,000 + 60 + 2$$

41. Draw lines to match the fraction with the decimal.

0.37 $\frac{3}{10}$

0.54 $\frac{5}{10}$

0.5 $\frac{54}{100}$

0.3 $\frac{37}{100}$

42. Leah wrote a 5-digit number on a piece of paper. She gave her friend Karen these clues to find the number.

What number did Leah write?

a. The 3 is in the place that is ten times greater than the place where the 5 is.

b. The 5 is in the place that is one hundred times less than the place where the 8 is.

c. The 2 is in the place that is ten times less than the place where the 5 is.

d. The 9 is in the place that is ten times greater than the place where the 8 is.

98,352

page CC 81

---

43. Draw a line of symmetry on this image.

44. Joni's mother is an event planner, She is planning a dinner for 432 guests. The banquet room has small round tables that seat 6 guests and large round tables that seat 10 guests.

a. How many tables will Joni's mother need if she uses the small tables? Write an equation to find the number of small tables. Use the letter s to represent the small tables. Then find the solution.

$$s = 432 \div 6;\ 72 \text{ tables}$$

b. How many tables will Joni's mother need if she uses the large tables? Write an equation to find the number of large tables. Use the letter l to represent the large tables.

$$l = 432 \div 10;\ 44 \text{ tables}$$

45. Draw models to show that $\frac{2}{3} = \frac{4}{6}$.

$$\frac{2}{3} \qquad\qquad \frac{4}{6}$$

In both circles, the size of the shaded region is the same.

page CC 82

Name _____

Performance Task 1

Camp Walkie-Talkies

Part A

The treasurer of a camp has a $1,000 budget to buy walkie-talkies for 56 campers. Each camper must have a walkie-talkie. The camp treasurer has narrowed down the choices to two models, Model A and Model B.

Each model has different prices depending on how they are ordered. The prices, including tax, for Model A and Model B are shown below.

Walkie-Talkie Model A   **Walkie-Talkie Model B**

Box with 6 pair—$34/pair   Box with 24 pair—$33/pair
1 pair—$42/pair   1 pair—$53/pair

1. Which model can the camp treasurer order with his $1,000 budget? Show and explain your work. Use a model to explain your calculations.

The camp treasurer can buy enough walkie talkies of only Model A for $1,000. Model B would cost more than $1,000.

page CC 83

Part B

The director of the same camp wants to make sure that when the older campers go on their 6-day hike, they will be able to use the new walkie-talkies during each day of the hike. She learns that both models have 15 hours of talk time (the amount of time a person can talk without recharging batteries). She will direct the camp counselors to set a limit on the number of minutes the campers can use the walkie-talkies each day of the hike.

2. How long can each camper use his or her walkie-talkie each day if it is used for the same amount of time each day?

Each camper can use his or her walkie-talkie for 150 minutes each day.

15 hours × 60 minutes = 900 minutes of talk time

900 minutes ÷ 6 days = 150 minutes/day

3. Write an equation to show how you solved the problem in Question 2. Let t = the amount of time a camper can use the walkie-talkie each day.

t = 900 ÷ 6

page CC 84

Name _____

Performance Task 2
Animal Shelter Volunteers
Part A

Roshanna and LeShan volunteer at their local animal shelter on Wednesdays after school. At the shelter they feed the dogs their afternoon meal according to the amounts of food given in the table below.

Other volunteers feed the dogs the same amounts in the morning. Each dog eats the same brand and type of food as the other dogs.

Dog	Amount of Dog Food per meal
Dante	$\frac{2}{3}$ cup
Shaggy	$\frac{1}{2}$ cup
Tessa	$\frac{3}{4}$ cup
Milo	$\frac{2}{3}$ cup
Sasha	$\frac{1}{2}$ cup
Bubba	$\frac{3}{4}$ cup

1. How much dog food does the shelter use each day to feed Tessa and Bubba? Use an equation and pictures of fraction models to support your answer.

   3 cups. $2 \times 2 \times \frac{3}{4} = \frac{12}{4} = 3$ cups of dog food

2. How much dog food does the shelter use each week to feed Dante and Milo?

   $18\frac{2}{3}$ cups each week.

page CC 85

Part B

Alia also volunteers at the same shelter. She feeds the cats in the shelter. The table shows the amount of food she gives to each cat each day.

Cat	Amount of Cat Food
Rascal	$\frac{5}{8}$ cup
Baggie	$\frac{1}{2}$ cup
Tabitha	$\frac{3}{4}$ cup
Tiger	$\frac{2}{3}$ cup

3. Compare the amount of food Rascal eats in a day with the amount of food Baggie eats in a day. Give two different comparisons. Show visual models to support your comparisons. Use the > sign in one comparison and the < sign in the other comparison.

   Rascal eats more food than Baggie. $\frac{5}{8} > \frac{1}{2}$ and $\frac{1}{2} < \frac{5}{8}$. Check students' drawings.

4. Alia feeds the cats in order of the amount of cat food that they are fed. She starts with the cat who gets the least amount of food. In what order does Alia feed all of the cats?

   Baggie, Rascal, Tiger, Tabitha.

page CC 86

Name _____

Practice for Common Core Assessment 2

1. Use the protractor to draw an angle of 120°. One side of the angle is drawn for you.

2. Circle all of the fractions that are less than $\frac{3}{8}$.

    ⃝$\frac{3}{10}$ $\frac{3}{4}$ ⃝$\frac{3}{9}$ ⃝$\frac{3}{12}$ $\frac{3}{5}$ $\frac{3}{6}$ ⃝$\frac{3}{20}$ $\frac{3}{3}$

3. An electronic system counts all of the vehicles that cross the Adams Bridge. The chart shows the number of vehicles that crossed the bridge for three days in May.

Day	Vehicles
May 1	3409
May 2	1288
May 3	2518

   What is the total number of vehicles that crossed the bridge during these three days?

   7215 vehicles

page CC 87

---

4. Tell whether the equation below is true. Use models to explain your answer. $\frac{2}{10} \stackrel{?}{=} \frac{22}{100}$.

   No, the equation is not true. $\frac{22}{100}$ is greater than $\frac{2}{10}$.

5. Anna and Jasmine competed in a race. Anna finished in $5\frac{1}{4}$ minutes. Jasmine finished in $4\frac{3}{4}$ minutes. How much longer was Anna running?

   $\frac{1}{2}$ minute, or 30 seconds

6. A farmer has 52 red hens, which is 4 times the number of her white hens.

   Write an equation that can be used to find the number of white hens at the farm. Use W to represent the white hens.

   $52 = 4 \times W$

page CC 88

7. In the figure below, which two lines are parallel?

(A) $\overline{AB}$ and $\overline{DE}$

B $\overline{AB}$ and $\overline{CD}$

C $\overline{BC}$ and $\overline{DE}$

D $\overline{AF}$ and $\overline{DE}$

8. A truck driver wants to drive a total of 1,845 miles in 5 days. For each day's mileage to be the same, how many miles should she drive each day? Explain how you found your answer.

369 miles each day; Check students' explanations.

9. Write an inequality comparing 15.02 and 14.86. Explain how you know which number is greater.

15.02 > 14.86; Check students' explanations.

page CC 89

---

10. A scout troop buys 4 large pizzas, each divided into 8 equal sections. The scouts eat 5 slices from each pizza.

a. Draw a model to match the problem situation.

b. Write an equation that matches your model.

$$4 \times \frac{5}{8} = ?$$

c. Did the scouts eat more or less than 3 whole pizzas?

The scouts ate less than 3 whole pizzas. They ate 20 slices, or $\frac{20}{8}$ of the pizza, which is $2\frac{1}{2}$ pizzas.

11. Frieda gathered 91 red peppers from her garden, 7 times greater than the number of yellow peppers that she gathered.

a. Write an equation that can be used to find the number of yellow peppers Frieda gathered from her garden. Use the letter y to represent the number of yellow peppers.

$91 = 7 \times y$

b. How many yellow peppers did Frieda gather from her garden?

13

page CC 90

---

12. Subtract 128.7 from 300.1.

171.4

13. Find a fraction that is equal to $\frac{2}{6}$. Draw models to show that the two fractions are equivalent.

Check students' answers. Accept any equivalent fraction.

14. Write the fraction $\frac{9}{10}$ as a decimal.

0.9

15. What is 63,492 rounded to the nearest thousand? Explain your answer.

63,000; Check students' explanations.

page CC 91

---

16. As shown in the diagram, angle *ABD* measures 23° and angle *DBC* measures 78°. What is the measurement of angle *ABC*?

101°

17. Subtract $2\frac{1}{4}$ from $7\frac{3}{8}$.

$5\frac{1}{8}$

18. A scientist collected some insects and measured their lengths. She recorded their lengths in a table.

Insect	A	B	C	D	E	F	G	H	I	J
Length (in.)	$\frac{1}{4}$	$\frac{1}{2}$	$\frac{1}{2}$	$\frac{1}{4}$	$\frac{1}{4}$	$\frac{1}{2}$	$\frac{3}{8}$	$\frac{1}{4}$	$\frac{3}{8}$	$\frac{1}{2}$

a. Make a line plot of the data.

Length (in.)

b. How much longer is the longest insect than the shortest insect?

$\frac{1}{4}$ in.

c. How many insects are longer than $\frac{1}{4}$ inch?

6

page CC 92

19. Which of these statements about the number below is true?

6,263.2

A The first 6 represents a value that is 10 times greater than the second 6.
B The first 6 represents a value that is 100 times greater than the second 6.
C The first 2 represents a value that is 100 times greater than the second 2.
D The first 2 represents a value that is 10 times greater than the second 2.

20. Find the quotient.

$5,016 \div 9$

557 R3

21. List all of the factor pairs for the number 63.

$1 \times 63; 3 \times 21; 7 \times 9$

page CC 93

---

22. Red Airlines has passengers board an airplane in four groups. The chart shows the number of passengers in Groups A, B, and C on Flight 12 from New York to Atlanta. The airplane can hold 135 passengers.

Passengers on Red Airlines, Flight 12

Group A	34 passengers
Group B	29 passengers
Group C	38 passengers
Group D	?

If all seats are filled, how many passengers are in Group D? Write an equation and solve it.

$34 + 29 + 38 + ? = 135$
$? = 34$
Group D has 34 passengers.

23. The students in Ms. Simon's class have 4 times as many dogs as fish. The students have 5 more cats than fish.

a. Write an equation to compare the number of dogs and fish that the students in Ms. Simon's class have. Use d to represent the number of dogs and f to represent the number of fish.

$d = 4 \times f$

b. Write an equation to compare the number of cats and fish that the students in Ms. Simon's class have. Use c to represent the number of cats and f to represent the number of fish.

$c = 5 + f$

c. Can you write an equation that compares the number of cats and dogs that the students in Ms. Simon's class have? Explain your answer.

No, I do not know how many cats or dogs the students have, so I cannot compare them to each other. For example, there could be 4 fish, 9 cats, and 16 dogs, or there could be 1 fish, 5 cats and 4 dogs.

page CC 94

---

24. Write a number statement to compare the numbers 8,257 and 7,789. Explain how you know which number is greater.

$7,789 < 8,257$

Check students' explanations.

25. Which of these triangles has one right angle?

A

B

C

D

page CC 95

---

26. What is the product of 3092 and 7?

21,644

27. Place these fractions on the number line below.

$\frac{1}{12}, \frac{5}{12}, \frac{7}{12}, \frac{11}{12}$

a. Compare $\frac{5}{12}$ and $\frac{7}{12}$ by comparing them to a benchmark fraction on the number line.

$\frac{7}{12}$ **is greater than** $\frac{1}{2}$ **and** $\frac{5}{12}$ **is less than** $\frac{1}{2}$ **so** $\frac{7}{12}$ **is greater than** $\frac{5}{12}$.

b. Compare $\frac{7}{12}$ and $\frac{11}{12}$ by comparing them to a benchmark fraction on the number line.

$\frac{7}{12}$ **is less than** $\frac{3}{4}$ **and** $\frac{11}{12}$ **is greater than** $\frac{3}{4}$ **so** $\frac{7}{12}$ **is less than** $\frac{11}{12}$.

page CC 96

28. Parker says that 2,872 rounded to the nearest hundred is 2,800.

  a. Is his answer correct? Explain how you know.

No. Sample explanation: The digit to the right of the hundreds place is greater than 5, so he should round up the digit in the hundreds place.

  b. What should be the answer?

2,900

29. Mary and José are painting a mural on a school wall. José paints $\frac{3}{8}$ of the mural and Mary paints $\frac{2}{8}$ of the wall. How much of the wall is left to paint?

  a. Draw a model to match the problem situation.

Check students' models.

  b. Write an equation to match the model you drew. Use x to represent the unpainted part of the wall.

$\frac{3}{8} + \frac{2}{8} + x = 1$

  c. Solve the equation you wrote. How much of the wall is left to paint?

$\frac{3}{8}$ of the wall

page CC 97

---

30. Mica's father has 48 feet of fencing. He wants to use it to put a fence around the family vegetable garden. Mica's father thinks the garden should be in the shape of a square.

  a. Draw a model of the garden.

Check students' drawings.

  b. Write an equation and solve to find the length of each side.

$4 \times S = 48.$
$S = 12$
Each side is 12 feet long.

31. Draw models to compare these fractions $\frac{7}{6}$, $\frac{7}{9}$, and 1.

$\frac{7}{9} < 1 < \frac{7}{6}$; Check students' models.

32. Omar measured a distance of 1.2 meters. Sue measured a distance of 0.9 meter. Use models to compare the distances. Which distance is greater?

1.2 meters

page CC 98

---

33. On May 1, Paula counted $2.00 in her piggy bank. She decided to add $1.50 to the bank every day, beginning the next day.

Complete the chart to show the total in the bank from May 1 to May 7.

Date	May 1	May 2	May 3	May 4	May 5	May 6	May 7
Total	$2.00	$3.50	$5.00	$6.50	$8.00	$9.50	$11.00

34. Tasha lined up 9 sticks end to end. Each stick has a length of $\frac{5}{6}$ yard.

  a. Write an equation for L, the total length of the 9 sticks.

$L = 9 \times \frac{5}{6}$

  b. Solve the equation to find L in yards.

$L = 9 \times \frac{5}{6}$
$L = \frac{9 \times 5}{6}$
$L = \frac{45}{6} = 7\frac{3}{6}$

The sticks have a total length of $7\frac{3}{6}$ yards, or $7\frac{1}{2}$ yards.

35. Find the product.

    $2,437 \times 7$

17,059

page CC 99

---

36. Deena and three of her friends are picking up trash from the beach. Each of them cleans a different part of the beach. Deena cleans $\frac{2}{5}$ of the beach. Each of her friends cleans $\frac{1}{5}$ of the beach. How much of the beach do they clean together?

$\frac{2}{5} + \frac{1}{5} + \frac{1}{5} + \frac{1}{5} = \frac{5}{5} = 1.$

37. A sack of potatoes weighs 5 pounds. How much do the potatoes weigh in ounces?

80 ounces

38. What is the sum of $\frac{2}{10}$ and $\frac{9}{100}$?

$\frac{29}{100}$

39. During one week at Trudy's Cafe, the staff sold 4 times as many banana muffins as chocolate chip muffins. They sold 76 banana muffins that week.

  a. Let C equal the number of chocolate chip muffins sold at the cafe. Write an equation that includes C.

$76 = 4 \times C$

  b. Solve the equation to find the number of chocolate chip muffins that they sold.

19 muffins

page CC 100

page CC 101

40. Write the expanded form of 7,160.

7,000 + 100 + 60

41. Draw lines to match the fraction with the decimal.

0.44 $\frac{6}{10}$

0.4 $\frac{6}{100}$

0.6 $\frac{4}{10}$

0.06 $\frac{4}{100}$

42. Many numbers can be made with the digits 9, 0, and 3. In which of the following numbers is the digit 9 in a place that is 10 times the place of the digit 3?

A   3,900

B   9,030

Ⓒ   930

D   903

page CC 102

43. Draw two lines of symmetry on the figure shown below.

44. Myra is storing songs on a music player. Each song lasts 4 minutes, and the player can hold 232 minutes of music.

a. How many songs can Myra store on the music player? Write an equation to find the number of songs. Use the letter s to represent the songs.

$$s = 232 \div 4;\ or\ 232 = s \times 4$$

b. Solve the equation to find the number of songs.

$$s = 58$$

45. Draw two circle models to show that $\frac{2}{8} = \frac{1}{4}$.

$\frac{2}{8}$ $\frac{1}{4}$

In both circles, the size of the shaded region is the same.

page CC 103

Name _____

Performance Task 3

Studying Animals

Part A

Ms. Gregoire's students go to the Science Museum once a month. This month they are studying birds and the eggs that different kinds of bird lay. Students will explore the size of the eggs compared to the size of the adult bird.

The museum bird specialist set out eggs from 15 different kinds of birds and told the students to sort the eggs into four groups. In Group 1 are eggs that are less than 3 centimeters in length; in Group 2 are eggs that are 3 centimeters and longer but less than 6 centimeters in length; in Group 3 are eggs that are 6 centimeters and longer, but less than 9 centimeters; and in Group 4 are eggs that are 9 centimeters and longer.

Type of Bird Egg	Length of Egg (in cm)
American Crow	3.97
American Robin	2.71
Bald Eagle	7.32
Barn Owl	4.14
California Condor	10.96
Canada Goose	9.25
Common Loon	7.91
Golden Eagle	7.23
Goldfinch	1.71
Great Horned Owl	5.12
Hummingbird	1.24
King Penguin	10.73
Red-Tailed Hawk	5.97
Whooping Crane	9.55
Wild Turkey	5.14

1. Which group will have the most eggs? Which group will have the fewest? List the groups in order from fewest to most eggs.

Group 2 has the most eggs with 5 eggs, and Groups 1 and 3 have the fewest, each with 3 eggs. In order from fewest to most the Groups are 1, 3, 4, 2

2. Explain how you sorted the eggs into the groups.

Check students' explanations.

page CC 104

Part B

Alfredo, the Museum bird specialist has asked Ms. Gregoire's students to help him count the number of bird eggs in his collection so he can place an order for more eggs. The table below shows how many of different bird eggs the students counted. Alfredo started to fill in the rest of the table to show how many eggs he needs and how many he needs to order to have the number he needs.

3. Complete the table for Alfredo.

Type of Bird Egg	Egg Count	Number of Eggs Needed	Number of Eggs Needed	Number of Eggs to Order
American Crow	5	3 more	8	3
American Robin	8	2 times as many	16	8
Bald Eagle	3	3 times as many	9	6
Barn Owl	4	2 more	6	2
California Condor	2	4 times as many	8	6
Goldfinch	7	5 more	12	5
Great Horned Owl	5	2 times as many	10	5
King Penguin	4	4 more	8	4
Red-Tailed Hawk	3	4 times as many	12	9
Wild Turkey	8	4 more	12	4

4. Which operations did you use to complete the table. Explain how you knew which operation to use.

Check students' explanations. They should name addition and multiplication as the operations they used.

Name _____

Performance Task 4
Arts and Crafts Design
Part A

Mr. Jones, the art teacher at Gifford Elementary School, is having his fourth-grade classes design their own stained glass windows using geometric figures. Before designing their own windows, the students will study some design samples of stained glass. Mr. Jones has given his students the design on the right to study.

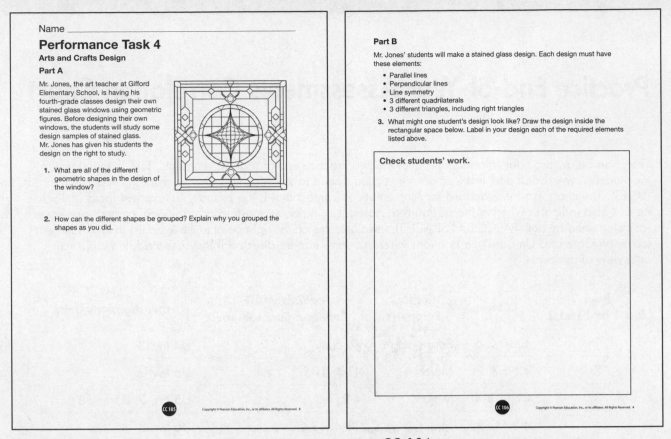

1. What are all of the different geometric shapes in the design of the window?

2. How can the different shapes be grouped? Explain why you grouped the shapes as you did.

page CC 105

Part B

Mr. Jones' students will make a stained glass design. Each design must have these elements:

- Parallel lines
- Perpendicular lines
- Line symmetry
- 3 different quadrilaterals
- 3 different triangles, including right triangles

3. What might one student's design look like? Draw the design inside the rectangular space below. Label in your design each of the required elements listed above.

Check students' work.

page CC 106

Practice End-of-Year Assessments Correlation Chart

Test 1 and Test 2

The chart below provides information about the two Practice End-of-Year Assessments, Test 1, found in the students' workbook and Test 2, a secure version, found in this Teacher's Guide, starting on page CC 87. The chart lists the Standard for Mathematical Content that is the primary assessment focus of each item. It also indicates whether the standard assessed is a major, supporting or additional content emphasis (as determined by both PARCC and SBAC). The two columns on the right point to the lesson(s) in enVisionMATH Common Core and Units in Investigations where students can be directed if they need additional practice or review of concepts.

Item Test 1 and Test 2	CCSS	Content Emphasis	enVisionMATH Common Core Lessons	Investigations Units
1	4.MD.C.6	Supporting	16-5	U4 Inv. 3
2	4.NF.A.2	Major	11-4, 11-5	U6 Inv. 2
3	4.NBT.B.4	Major	4-2, 4-3	U5 Inv. 2; U5 Inv. 3
4	4.NF.C.5	Major	13-4, 13-6	U6 Inv. 3
5	4.MD.A.2	Supporting	15-2	U4 Inv. 1
6	4.OA.A.1	Major	1-10	U1 Inv. 1
7	4.G.A.1	Additional	16-1, 16-2	U4 Inv. 2
8	4.NBT.B.6	Major	9-4, 9-5, 10-6, 10-7	U3 Inv. 2; U8 Inv. 3
9	4.NF.C.7	Major	13-7, 13-8	U6 Inv. 3
10	4.NF.B.4	Major	13-1, 13-2, 13-3	U6 Inv. 3A
11	4.OA.A.1	Major	1-1, 1-3, 1-7, 1-10	U1 Inv. 1; U1 Inv. 3
12	4.NBT.B.4	Major	4-4, 4-5	U5 Inv. 1; U5 Inv. 4
13	4.NF.A.1	Major	11-4, 11-5, 11-8	U6 Inv. 1; U6 Inv. 2
14	4.NF.C.6	Major	13-4, 13-6	U6 Inv. 3
15	4.NBT.A.3	Major	3-5	U5 Inv. 1; U5 Inv. 3
16	4.MD.C.7	Additional	16-6	U4 Inv. 3
17	4.NF.B.3	Major	12-1	U6 Inv. 2
18	4.MD.B.4	Supporting	15-4	U6 Inv. 2; U9 Inv. 3
19	4.NBT.A.1	Major	3-1, 3-2, 3-6	U5 Inv. 3
20	4.NBT.B.6	Major	10-1, 10-2, 10-3, 10-4, 10-5, 10-6, 10-7	U3 Inv. 2; U8 Inv. 3

Item Test 1 and Test 2	CCSS	Content Emphasis	enVisionMATH Common Core Lessons	Investigations Units
21	4.OA.B.4	Supporting	11-1	U1 Inv. 3; U3 Inv. 1
22	4.OA.A.3	Major	1-10, 4-1, 4-2, 4-3	U1 Inv. 1
23	4.OA.A.2	Major	1-10, 9-6	U1 Inv. 1; U1 Inv. 3
24	4.NBT.A.2	Major	3-2, 3-3	U5 Inv. 1; U5 Inv. 3
25	4.G.A.2	Additional	16-5, 16-7, 16-9	U4 Inv. 2
26	4.NBT.B.5	Major	6-1, 6-2, 6-3, 6-4, 6-5	U3 Inv. 1; U3 Inv. 3
27	4.NF.A.2	Major	11-5, 11-6, 11-7	U6 Inv. 2
28	4.NBT.A.3	Major	3-5	U5 Inv. 1; U5 Inv. 3
29	4.NF.B.3	Major	12-1, 12-2, 12-3, 12-4	U6 Inv. 1; U6 Inv. 2
30	4.MD.A.3	Supporting	15-1	U4 Inv. 4
31	4.NF.A.2	Major	11-5, 11-6, 11-7	U6 Inv. 1; U6 Inv. 2
32	4.NF.C.7	Major	13-7, 13-8	U6 Inv. 3
33	4.OA.C.5	Additional	1-2, 1-5, 2-1, 2-2, 2-3, 2-4	U8 Inv. 2; U9 Inv. 2
34	4.NF.B.4	Major	13-1, 13-2, 13-3	U6 Inv. 3A
35	4.NBT.B.5	Major	6-1, 6-2, 6-3, 6-4, 6-5	U3 Inv. 1; U3 Inv. 3
36	4.NF.B.3	Major	12-1, 12-2	U6 Inv. 1; U6 Inv. 2
37	4.MD.A.1	Supporting	14-8, 14-9	U7 Inv. 3; U9 Inv. 3
38	4.NF.C.5	Major	13-4, 13-5, 13-6	U6 Inv. 3
39	4.OA.A.2	Major	1-10, 9-6	U1 Inv. 1; U1 Inv. 3
40	4.NBT.A.2	Major	3-1, 3-2	U5 Inv. 2; U5 Inv. 3
41	4.NF.C.6	Major	13-4, 13-6	U6 Inv. 3
42	4.NBT.A.1	Major	3-1, 3-2	U5 Inv. 3
43	4.G.A.3	Additional	16-10	U4 Inv. 4
44	4.OA.A.3	Major	9-1, 9-2, 9-3, 9-6	U3 Inv. 2; U8 Inv. 3
45	4.NF.A.1	Major	11-4	U6 Inv. 1; U6 Inv. 2

Performance Tasks Scoring Rubrics

Performance Task 1 – Camp Walkie-Talkies

Primary Content Domains and Clusters

Operations and Algebraic Thinking: Use the four operations with whole numbers to solve problems. (4.OA.A.2, 4.OA.A.3)

Secondary Content Domains and Clusters

Number and Operations in Base Ten: Use place value understanding and properties of operations to perform multi-digit arithmetic. (4.NBT.B.5, 4.NBT.B.6)

Math Practices Focus

MP 1, 2, 4, 7

Scoring Rubric

1	**Selects a model and justifies the selection.**	10
	Chooses the model that will fit the budget.	
	Justifies the choice.	
	Uses a model to explain calculations.	
2	**Determines the number of minutes of use per day.**	5
	Multiplies to find the amount of minutes.	
	Divides to find the minutes per day.	
3	**Writes an accurate equation.**	5
	Writes a correct equation that includes *t* as the variable.	
TOTAL		20

Performance Task 2 – Animal Shelter Volunteers

Primary Content Domains and Clusters

Number and Operations – Fractions: Extend understanding of fraction equivalence and ordering. (4.NF.A.1, 4.NF.A.2); Build fractions from unit fractions by applying and extending previous understandings of operations on whole numbers. (4.NF.B.3, 4.NF.B.4)

Secondary Content Domains and Clusters

Measurement and Data: Solve problems involving measurement and conversion of measurements from a larger unit to a smaller unit. (4.MD.A.2)

Math Practices Focus

MP 1, 2, 3, 4, 6, 7, 8

Scoring Rubric

1	**Determines the amount of the food for the two dogs.**	6
	Uses appropriate operations to calculate the amount of dog food used.	
	Writes an appropriate equation to model the situation.	
	Shows models of the fractions.	
2	**Determines the amount of the food for the two dogs.**	4
	Uses appropriate operations to calculate the amount of dog food used.	
3	**Compares two fractions appropriately and accurately.**	6
	Writes two inequalities comparing the correct amounts.	
	Show visual models supporting the comparisons.	
4	**Puts the names in the correct order.**	4
	Orders the 4 names by the amount of food, from least to greatest.	
TOTAL		20

Performance Task 3 – Studying Animals

Primary Content Domains and Clusters

Number and Operations – Fractions: Understand decimal notation for fractions, and compare decimal fractions. (4.NF.C.7)

Secondary Content Domains and Clusters

Operations and Algebraic Thinking: Use four operations with whole numbers to solve problems. (4.OA.A.1, 4.OA.A.3)

Math Practices Focus

MP 1, 2, 4, 6, 7, 8

Scoring Rubric

1	**Identifies the number of eggs in each group and answers each question.**	5
	Identifies the group with most and the group with fewest eggs.	
	Puts the groups in order by number of eggs from fewest to most.	
2	**Explains sorting into groups.**	5
	Explains why numbers were in each of the 4 groups.	
3	**Completes the table correctly.**	5
	Calculates the correct number of eggs needed and eggs to order for each type of bird egg.	
4	**Explains operations used to complete table.**	5
	Identifies the correct operations.	
	Explains how multiplication, addition, and subtraction were used.	
TOTAL		**20**

Performance Task 4 – Arts and Crafts Design

Primary Content Domains and Clusters

Geometry: Draw and identify lines and angles, and classify shapes by properties of their lines and angles. (4.G.A.1, 4.G.A.2, 4.G.A.3)

Math Practices Focus

MP 1, 4, 6, 7, 8

Scoring Rubric

1	Identifies the different geometric shapes in the design.	4
	Names at least 80% of the different shapes in the design shown.	
2	Classifies all of the identified shapes into several categories.	6
	Makes accurate sorting of shapes into categories.	
	Justifies the sorting of the shapes.	
3	Draws a design including all of the required elements.	10
	Draws each of the elements described in the list.	
	Labels each of the required elements.	
TOTAL		20